A PAGEANT OF
HORSES

Text adapted by Pola Weiss
from **A.-E. Brehm**
Translated by Anthony Werner

Minerva

Contents

© Editions Minerva, S.A., Genève, 1974
Printed in England
by Sir Joseph Causton and Son Ltd.,
London and Eastleigh

1. The origin of horses

When was the animal which is so worthy of the adjectives "noble" and "useful", in all the forms in which we know it, first mastered, and to whom do we owe this mastery?

There is nothing to enlighten us on this point: nothing indicates when man first subjugated horses, nor do we even know where they were first tamed. But it is believed that horses were turned into domestic animals by the peoples of Central Asia, and it was from there that they were exported to the Far East and China, on the one hand, and to the South and West, on the other. They still exist in their wild state in that region, inhabiting the steppes and mountains, where they are found in considerable numbers. Presumably, domestic horses often intermingled with these wild herds, but the bulk of the equine population is certainly in its original state. Zoology is helped here by philology, for the various terms used for horses in Western languages all derive from Zend and Sanskrit, in other words, languages of Central Asia; it is therefore from this ancient center of advanced civilization that the species has come down to us, together with the names which it still bears.

Whether or not this view is correct, history first finds these animals in Egypt. They are depicted on the oldest hieroglyphs carrying

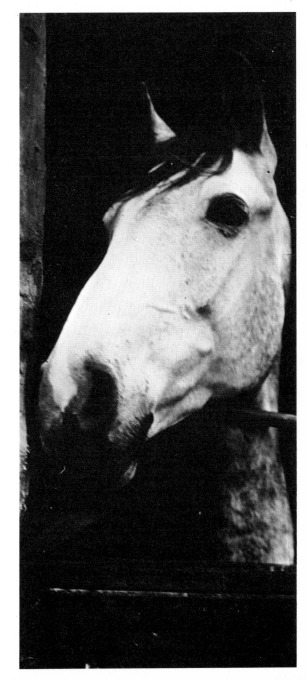

men in the thick of battle and drawing chariots. In Persia and India, too, the horse has been man's companion from the beginning of historical times.

The Chinese, who according to their literature had also obtained horses from abroad, were already using them in military expeditions more than two thousand years before the birth of Christ.

The Hebrews had horses only about the time of David and Solomon. Abraham, Isaac and Jacob owned mules, which are mentioned with camels and sheep among their possessions, but they do not appear to have raised horses or even to have cared about them. It is remarkable that horses are not mentioned in Jewish books until the era of Joseph; the conclusion would seem to be that the Hebrews only owned these animals from the time of the return from Egypt, and may have brought them back from there.

"At the time of Moses", writes a historian, "the Israelites did not use them at all, even in battle, and the law-giver recommends that, when going to war, they should not be afraid of their enemies' horses or chariots but should trust in the God of Israel; but this was not always the case, and the Book of Samuel already mentions Jonathan's rider; it also relates that David, conqueror of Hadadezer, son of Rehob, king of Zobah, on the Euphrates, captured 700 horsemen from him, and that he *houghed all the chariot horses but reserved of them for an hundred chariots.*

"Soon afterwards, compliance with the ancient laws had to be relaxed again in the light of the new requirements of a civilization markedly improved by its relations with enlightened peoples; thus, we read elsewhere: 'And Solomon had forty thousand horses for his chariots and twelve thousand horsemen'. And further on: 'And Solomon gathered together chariots and horsemen: and he had a thousand and four hundred chariots, and twelve thousand horsemen, whom he bestowed in the cities for chariots, and with the king at Jerusalem'.

"The same book tells us where the horses came from, and even their value. They came partly from Egypt and Coa, where they were bought at a fixed price. A four-horse chariot from Egypt cost Solomon six hundred shekels of silver, and a horse (no doubt a stallion) a hundred and fifty; and all the kings of the Hittites and of Syria also sold him horses."

The Bible also gives an admirable description of Job's horse.

In Europe, the domestication of the equine species goes back far beyond the heroic times of Greece. Homer mentions the many stud-farms owned by Priam, and attributes 3,000 mares and a similar number of magnificent colts to Erichthonius, one of the ancestors of the last king of Troy.

The horses used most successfully by the Greeks were certainly those from Asia Minor and Egypt, because the magnificent remains of bas-reliefs in the Parthenon show that at Pericles' time the Athenians had very elegant horses, and we know from various authors that the horses which ran in the Olympic Games came from Cappadocia and neighbouring regions.

It is not only on the bas-reliefs of its monuments that Greek art depicted horses so excellently: they are also found on a great many medallions. The horse had also become the symbol of Carthage, and Winckelmann mentions medallions from that city on which it is depicted next to a palm-tree. Choiseul refers to other medallions, especially those

from Thessalonica, Maronea and Cyma, bearing the same emblem.

It has been said that the art of mounting horses was invented by the Scythians—today the Tatars—and that when they arrived in Thrace the Greeks were so frightened that they believed the man and the animal were a single body: this is even said to be the origin of the tale of the centaurs. It is known that the Mexicans had the same fears and made the same mistake when they first saw the Spanish horsemen unleashed against them by Cortes.

If nothing can tell us where and when the horse was first mastered, is it possible at least to ascertain its origin? Does it derive from one species or several?

Here, too, there is complete ignorance, which cannot be dispelled by tradition, history or science. Those who postulate a single originating species are perhaps on as firm ground as those who say that there were more. In Fitzinger's view, most of our various breeds are descended from three primeval horses—the *tarpan*, the *hairless horse* and the *light horse*—and two conjectural varieties, completely unknown in practice—the *heavy horse* and the *dwarf horse*.

2. Wild horses

Horses in their wild state are not as handsome as domesticated horses: their heads are larger and their bones protude more.

They roam in herds led by a male which, as the courageous head of the group, confronts all dangers first. These herds have no fixed refuge when they want to rest; they are very afraid of thunderstorms, and when thunder starts to roll they may be seen fleeing, frightened, until they find shelter or the thunder stops.

The many herds of horses which may still be found today in the steppes of Upper Asia differ little from those which we know, though it is not clear whether they are the descendants or ancestors of domestic horses. Some look exactly like wild animals, while others are only horses which have reverted to the wild state, like those of the *llanos* of South America.

The tarpan, regarded by the Tatars and the Cossacks as a genuinely wild animal, is of medium size and rather thin.

It has slim, but strong and long limbs, a thin and rather long neck, a relatively broad head, a bulging forehead, pointed ears slanting forwards, and small, lively eyes sparkling with mischief. Its hoofs are thin and pointed; its hair in summer is coarse, short, wavy and almost frizzy, especially on the hind legs; in winter, it is thick, strong, and long,

especially around the neck, where it forms a sort of beard. Its mane is short, thick, bushy and frizzy. Its tail is of medium length. Its coat is brown or fawn-colored in summer and lighter, almost white, in winter; its tail and mane are dark. There are no gray tarpans, and black ones are rare.

The tarpan originated in the regions between the Aral Sea and the south side of the mountains of Upper Asia. It is found in large numbers in all the steppes of Mongolia, in the Gobi Desert, in the forests along the upper reaches of the Hoang-ho River and in the mountains of northern India. It seems to have been more widespread in earlier times and to have been found in Siberia, and even European Russia, about two hundred years ago.

Tarpans are always seen in herds of several hundred. Each herd is subdivided into small families, each headed by a stallion. These herds roam the vast steppes in all directions and usually move into the wind. When there is snow, tarpans climb into the mountains and forests, scraping away the snow in order to graze. Explorers have come across them at a height of 18,000 feet, where they were very mistrustful and fearful. Tarpans are considered to be the most cautious of the steppe animals. Heads raised, ears pricked and nostrils open, they look all around and can always recognize an enemy's approach in time.

The stallion is the head of the group: he ensures its safety, but in return demands obedience. He drives off young males, who are condemned to follow the herd at a distance until they have gathered some mares around them. As soon as the herd becomes aware of something unfamiliar, its leader snorts, moves his ears and runs with his head held high; if he smells danger, he whinnies loudly and the entire group gallops away, the mares leading and the stallions bringing up the rear to protect the withdrawal. The mares often disappear as if by magic: they have hidden in a hollow and are waiting to see what happens. The stallions are not afraid of carnivora: they rush at wolves and beat them with their forelegs. It used to be said that to resist their enemies they form a circle, with their heads towards the center, and kick backwards continuously, but this story has long been refuted. But it is true that the stallions form a circle around the mares and foals when a beast of prey approaches. A bear may from time to time eat a tarpan, but wolves are always put to flight.

Stallions engage in violent fights with each other: young stallions always have to buy their rights through fierce duels.

The inhabitants of the steppes, who raise horses, fear tarpans more than wolves because of the damage they cause. As soon as these wild horses catch sight of a carriage drawn by domesticated horses which were formerly wild like them, they run towards it: the horses hardly have time to recognize them by their whinnying before they are surrounded and dragged away, by force if necessary.

Woe betide the people in the carriage! Oblivious of the cries and blows of the attendants, the steppe-horses, driven to rage, kick and bite the carriages to pieces, tear off their friends' harnesses and free them; then, neighing for joy, they take them away in triumph.

Tarpans are difficult to tame. Their liveliness, strength and ferocity defy all the subtlety of the Mongols themselves.

They do not take well to captivity; most captive tarpans die in the second year. Even foals can be tamed only partially: they always remain wild and disobedient. They cannot be used for riding: the most that can be done is to harness them in pairs to a carriage and even then they give plenty of trouble to the other horse and the driver.

Muzins are domestic horses which have returned to the feral state. They can be recognized by their awkward gait. When they include tarpan stallions—which is rare—these stallions take charge of the herd. Muzins also entice domestic horses and urge them to share their freedom. It is said that they will cross the widest watercourses and ponds, from which tarpans draw back.

The life of horses of the Asiatic steppes is no more enviable than that of their forerunners. They are of extremely pure stock and achieve a high degree of perfection not in the beauty of their form but in their strength and vigor. It is alleged that the superb neck and withers which this horse acquires when in human hands result from the fact that it is often housed in a stable with a window in the roof, and the animal thus becomes accustomed to looking up and acquires a noble bearing.

The steppe-horse is the favorite animal of Tatars. It is used more for riding than for traction; but only a few are kept at home for riding and fed with hay and barley. The rest live on the steppe all year round in large herds and have to find their own food. Hordes of 1,000 to 2,000 of these horses are often seen together; free, proud and lively, no man has ever tamed or humiliated them. In bad weather, storms and snow, they scatter, often over wide areas, and it takes several days to find them again. But the Tatars know that these horses always move into the wind, and so they know in which direction to look for them.

In a few rare cases, herdsmen keep watch over these horses. They are brought back to the village every twenty-four hours and the mares are milked. A child can bring back the entire herd, because as soon as the horses realize that they must go to be milked they gather like sheep. During the heat of summer they do not eat: they form a circle, heads towards the centre, to give each other a little shade, and swish their tails unceasingly. If a slight breeze starts to blow they scatter over the steppe, lifting their heads to breathe in the wind. A stallion is accompanied by several mares. Often, the leader of a herd tries to take away a mare from another herd: this leads to violent, and sometimes fatal, struggles between the abductors and the stallion of the herd concerned. The participants rear up on their hind legs, advance towards each other, and bite and kick with force enough to break each other's bones.

If a Tatar wishes to break an adult horse for riding, he begins by capturing it with a lasso; then several others come to help him try and tie the horse's legs. When this has been done, they turn it over, and while some of them hold it down, the others put a harness and fetters on it: these consist of a band fixed to three of its feet so as to prevent it from running but not from standing or taking short steps. The horse is then put back on its feet and held by its ears while a special saddle, held in place by a strap, is put on its back; a Tatar sits on the animal's back behind this saddle, part of which projects and prevents him from falling; the fetters are then removed, the rider strikes his untamed mount and gives it its head, while another horseman follows and strikes the animal to prevent it pulling up short or veering to the side. This is done until the horse becomes tired, when its rider tries to guide it and bring it back to the village. There it is tied up in such a way that it may take a few steps but cannot lie down with its head on the ground, and is given only a few handfuls of hay. After one night like this it is given water and the same exercises are then resumed, but this time the horse is completely saddled. After a few days hunger and fatigue have fully tamed the animal, which becomes as docile as a sheep.

When traveling, horses are never tied up but are left free: they never sleep in a stable. During the day, they are made to cover long distances and cross the broadest rivers, for they can swim perfectly; in this case, their keepers follow by boat or in the water, clinging to the tail of one of them.

The steppe-horse is extremely useful to the Tatar. It carries him and his dwelling, it threshes his corn and it helps him to bring game to bay. Its skin and hair are used for various purposes, and its flesh, fat and offal can be eaten. To the Tatars, horsemeat is the finest dish. As a rule they only eat sick or newly dead horses. The tendons used to be used for sewing and were preferred to thread because they were more solid. Lakut brides offer their bridegrooms a cooked horse's head garnished with sausages made of the animal's flesh. Hairs from the tail fixed to a tree please the spirit of the forest.

The existence of the hairless horse, a rare and little-known animal, was only reported in the last century. It is the horse most like the Arabian. It is well built and of medium height; but apart from a few thick hairs over its skin it is completely naked. It may even be said that it has no mane and even less tail, for the latter term can hardly be used to describe the ten or twelve stiff and brittle hairs, each just over an inch long, which cover its caudal extremity. Its skin— sleek, tender, velvety and shiny—is dark gray or dun-colored. Careful observations have shown that the nakedness of the skin did not originate from any illness or action on the part of the owner.

This horse cannot be recommended as a domestic animal: its skin is so sensitive that it is injured by the lightest harness.

We have few details of the migrant horses of Africa. This horse, which the Arabs living along the banks of the River Niger call *Kumrah*, is very much like a pony: it is small, but well-proportioned; it has a large head, a broad forehead, rather large ears, indifferent eyes, a bushy tail and mane and flat hairs, except on the forehead, where they are woolly. The color of its coat is smokey gray or white.

In Roman times, this breed seems to have been quite widespread, but today it is found only in the thick mountain forests of West Africa. Its true habitat appears to be on the banks of the Niger.

It lives in small groups; it is very fearful and flees from danger, but, if forced to, it defends itself bravely, especially against beasts of prey. Its cry is somewhere between the neighing of a horse and the braying of a donkey. The natives capture and tame it. Although very wild at first, it can soon be tamed and broken.

There are large herds of migrant horses in South America, and several authors have given us interesting information about them.

One of them writes: "Pedro de Mendoza arrived with a fleet in 1535 and founded the city of Buenos Aires. Soon afterwards it was depopulated, because the inhabitants moved on to Paraguay, but the move was so disorganized and hasty that they could not take with them all the mares which they had brought from Andalusia and Tenerife, many of which they were compelled to abandon.

"Don Juan de Garay re-settled the city on August 11, 1580 with sixty inhabitants of Paraguay, who found a large number of wild horses, the offspring of these mares, there already, and started to tame those they could catch. Tax officials opposed this, claiming that the horses belonged to the king, and the incident led to legal proceedings. I have seen, in the Paraguayan archives, the judgement of 1596 stating that the tax authorities' claim was unfounded and deciding that the conquerors were the owners of any wild horses which they succeeded in breaking. This is the origin of the many wild horses which exist south of the River Plate."

Cimarrones, as these roving horses are called, are as big and as strong as domestic horses, but less handsome. Their heads and legs are thicker, their necks and ears longer. They are entirely brown or black, although black ones are rare.

Cimarrones now live in all pampas in large herds of up to 12,000. Each stallion gathers as many mares as it can but remains with them in the common herd, which has no recognized leader. These chestnut horses are harmful because they devastate the grasslands and, like tarpans, entice away domestic horses.

When they see domestic horses they run towards them, greet them by neighing and incorporate them into the herd without much resistance on their part. Travelers often used to find themselves in serious trouble because these cimarrones enticed their mounts away, and someone was always on the lookout to drive them off. They approach, not in battle line, but in single file like Indians. Often they form a large circle around the rider and are not easily frightened off; at other times, they pass by without paying any attention. Sometimes, they charge about blindly in the midst of a wagon-train. Fortunately, they do not emerge at night, either because they cannot see or because they cannot smell domestic horses.

Roads over which they have passed are covered with their dung for stretches of more than a mile. Almost certainly, they seek out roads on which to deposit their excrement, and since all horses tend to smell out the dung of their fellows and add their own to it, the heaps caused by this habit often constitute veritable hillocks.

A. Guinnard, a traveler who spent three years among the Patagonians, has given us some very interesting details about the roving horses of the area. "The horses of the pampas", he writes, "are usually of medium height and well built, quite easy to tame and almost indefatigable. I have often seen these animals, which are in no way inferior to the more handsome Andalusians, galloping for a whole day and a whole night without taking anything but water. The Indians tame them in a very brutal way: once lassoed, they up-end them on the ground and tie their feet together so as to be able easily to put a strap into their mouths; after the gums and lips have been scraped in order to make them more obedient to the pressure of this overly flexible bit, the strap

is firmly attached below the lower lip. They then saddle them and make them get up with two people holding them: one by the nostrils and an ear, the other at the hindquarters by a lasso restricting the movements of their hind legs. Then the trainer, armed with a large leather thong or a kind of very hard and heavy whip ending in a piece of wood for flogging the horse's sides and then its head, springs boldly on to the animal. At a given signal, his assistants, their movements perfectly co-ordinated, give the charger its head, and the horse usually bolts like a shot, not without plenty of lashing out and bucking. Some resist their rider's prodigious efforts to make them turn their heads to the left or the right and roll over, but despite their spirited resistance, they are usually docile enough to be mounted without a saddle after two or three days.

"The Indians tame them in this way at the age of about two and a half, when they also test their speed: they are made to cover a certain distance without taking another breath, and those which do not pass the test easily are deemed unsuitable for service and pitilessly condemned to be eaten."

Unlike the pampas of Argentina, Paraguay has no wild horses. According to the explorer Rengger, this is mainly due to a fly which deposits its eggs in the still bleeding navel of the new-born foal: this causes an ulcer which leads to death when the animal is abandoned to its own devices. In Paraguay, however, the independence in which horses live hardly differs from the wild state.

These horses, called *mustangs*, have been left so much to themselves that they have degenerated. They are of medium height, with a large head, long ears and thick joints. Only the head and the trunk are well-proportioned. Their coat is long in winter and short in summer. The mane and tail are always short and not very thick. Horses of this type which resemble their ancestors are only found in a few farms.

They are as swift as Andalusians and more resistant to fatigue. Rengger states that he often galloped fifteen or even thirty miles on one of these horses, in the blazing heat, without the animal being any the worse for wear.

South American horses are still often left to roam free. They spend the whole year out in the open. So that they do not wander too far away, they are brought together once a week, when any wounds are examined, cleaned and rubbed with cow-dung, and about every three years the tails and manes of the stallions are trimmed: this is all the care they get. Nobody thinks about improving the stock.

The pasturelands are bad, with only one kind of grass, which grows strongly in spring and gives the horses diarrhoea which tires them out. In summer and fall they recover and grow fat, but their "paunches" disappear as soon as they are put to work. Winter is their worst season. The grass is dry and all that the unfortunate beasts have to eat is stubble, softened slightly by rain. This food makes them want salt. When they are fed in the stable, they no longer need salt. Better nourished and cared for, they acquire a short and glossy coat, firm flesh and a noble, proud bearing in the space of a few months.

"Usually", says Rengger, "they live in particular areas to which they have become accustomed since their early days. Each stallion is given twelve to eighteen mares which he keeps with him and defends

against other stallions. If he is given too many, he lets them go. Foals stay with their mothers up to the age of three or four. As long as she is suckling them, the mother shows them the tenderest feelings. She often has to fight off female mules, which from time to time develop a kind of maternal love. When this happens, they try to take away a foal by stealth or by force, giving it their empty dugs to suck, and the unfortunate foal soon dies.

"When the young horses are two or three years old, a stallion is chosen, given some young fillies and accustomed to graze with them in a certain area. The other stallions are castrated and grouped in herds. The horses belonging to one herd never join another; they are so close to one another that it is very difficult to make a horse leave his fellows. When various herds are brought together—for example, when a farmer gathers in all his horses—the members of the same herd find each other very quickly. The stallion calls his mares by his whinnying, the geldings seek each other out, and each herd then returns to its own area. A group of a thousand horses will take less than fifteen minutes to form small units of between ten and thirty. I noticed that horses of the same size or color took to each other more than those of different size or color, and that foreign horses mostly form a group among themselves, not mixing with the native horses. These animals show the same attachment not only to others like themselves but also to their pasturelands. I have seen them cover very great distances in order to return to their usual haunts. It is equally curious sometimes to see the horses of an entire region leave, singly or in groups. This happens mainly when a drought is suddenly followed by rain; they are probably frightened by the hail which usually falls in the first storm.

"The senses of these semi-wild horses seem to be more highly developed than those of European horses. Their hearing is very sharp. At night, their ear movements show that they can hear the slightest noise, which may completely escape the rider. Their sight, like that of all horses, is rather weak, but their life of freedom accustoms them to recognizing objects from afar. Their sense of smell enables them to distinguish the things around them. They can nose out anything that seems strange. It is by their sense of smell that they recognize their rider, harness, place of saddling, etc., can find dry spots in marshland, and can find their way in the middle of the night or in fog. Good horses can smell their master as soon as he mounts, and I have seen some which would not carry a rider if he was not wearing a poncho or coat like the men who tamed and harnessed them. When something has frightened them, they are calmed by being given something to sniff.

"In years of drought, when the wells at which they are used to drinking dry up, they die of thirst rather than seek new ones; horned animals, on the other hand, often travel ten or twenty miles in search of water. Their tastes vary: some take immediately to forage and the stable diet, eating corn and

even meat that has been dried in the sun; others die rather than touch any food except ordinary grass. Their life in the open and the bites they receive from horseflies and mosquitoes dull their sense of touch.

"The Paraguayan horse is usually docile; but it is often spoiled by the ill-treatment it receives when being tamed. When it has reached the age of four or five, it is tied to a stake and, despite its resistance, saddled and harnessed. When this has been done, it is untied and a tamer immediately springs on to its back, wearing long, sharp spurs and carrying a large whip: he then rains blows onto the animal and makes it run through the fields until it reaches the point of exhaustion, can resist no longer and is compelled to obey. These exercises are repeated from time to time and the horse is regarded as broken in when it no longer bucks. It is not surprising that this treatment makes the horses vicious and stubborn — they rear up, buck, shy and try everything to unseat their rider. But if they are well treated, these same horses become very obedient, allow themselves to be taken without difficulty and voluntarily undertake the most tiring work.

"During the rainy season, when all the rivers are swollen and all the roads are under water, a good horse who has covered a particular road a few times will lead its rider through all these dangerous paths, not only during the day but also at night. If it is not pushed, it always advances cautiously, especially in unknown places. In marshland, it paws the ground with its forefeet at each step. This caution does not reveal any lack of courage, for the Paraguayan horse is a fearless animal. Guided by a good rider it faces danger unhesitatingly; it will rush at enraged bulls, plunge down a steep embankment into a river or run swiftly through the middle of a blazing steppe fire.

"All in all, these animals are exposed to few illnesses. If well fed and not forced, they live as long as European horses; but as good food and treatment are things they normally lack, a twelve-year-old horse is considered old."

Horses often used to be hunted in South America for their hides and meat. According to Darwin, a great many mares were regularly killed near Las Nacas solely for their hides. Buenos Aires was long lit by gas produced from the fat of horses killed solely for the use of this fat and for their hides.

"During my stay at Henderson", relates the famous naturalist and artist Audubon, "I made the acquaintance of a gentleman who had just returned from a visit to the area around the source of the river Arkansas. There he had bought a wild horse, captured quite recently, which was descended from horses originally brought from Spain and subsequently set free in the vast prairies of Mexico. The animal was not good-looking, far from it; it had a large head with a bump in the middle of the forehead; its thick, shaggy mane hung down from its neck to its chest, and its tail, which was too meagre to be called billowing, almost trailed along the ground; on the other hand, it had a broad breast and fine, wiry legs, and its eyes, like its nostrils, were bright with fire, vigor and great stamina. It had never been iron-shod, and although it had been overtaxed on a recent long journey, its black shoes had come to no harm. Its color was close to bay; its legs were darker, becoming increasingly brown until they were almost black at the bottom. I asked how much it might be worth

to the Osage Indians, and the owner told me that, considering that the animal was only four years old, he had had to exchange various articles worth about 35 dollars for it, including the saddle wood and buffalo-hide harness; he added that he had never mounted a better one, and did not doubt that, well fed, it had carried its master between 35 and 40 miles a day for a month—at least, that was the rate at which he himself had been traveling, without allowing it any other fodder except prairie-grass and lowland reeds. It was only after crossing the Mississippi at Natchez that he had given it corn.' Now that I have ended my trip', he said, 'I don't need him any more and would like to sell him. I think he would make a good hunter: he gives a very gentle ride, does not get tired and is of a mettle that I have rarely seen.' I was in fact looking for a horse with just the qualities which he was praising in his own, and I asked him if I could try it. 'Try him, Sir, but of course! And if you would like to feed him and take care of him, you are free to keep him for a month.' Consequently, I put the horse in the stables and saw to it that he was fed.

"Two hours later, I took my gun, mounted the prairie charger and set off for the woods. It was not long before I noticed that he was very sensitive to the spur; I also observed that he did indeed walk perfectly without getting tired and without causing his rider any discomfort. I wanted to find out immediately what I could expect of him in a deer or bear hunt by making him jump over the stump of a tree several feet in diameter. I gave him free rein, pressed his flanks with my legs and did not use the spur; and the intelligent animal, apparently realizing he was being tested, leapt over the stump as

lightly as an elk. I turned at the gallop, made him jump several times in succession, and always got the same result. Convinced now that with this horse I need not fear any obstacles of this kind in the woods, I resolved to test his strength, and to this end headed towards a swamp which I knew to be muddy and very difficult. He entered it, sniffing the water as if to ascertain its depth, thus showing pleasing caution and wisdom. I then rode him in different directions right through, and found him willing, sure-footed and decisive. Can he swim? I wondered: for some excellent horses cannot swim at all but lie down on their side as if to float along on the current, so that the rider himself has to start swimming and pulling the horse towards the bank if he does not want to abandon it. The Ohio was not far off; I pushed him right into the middle of the river, and he began to take the stream diagonally, his head well above the surface and his nostrils dilated, without making anything at all like the usual whinnying noise of many horses in similar situations. I rode him back and forth, sometimes downstream, sometimes in exactly the opposite direction; and finally, finding him completely to my liking, I reached the bank again, where he stopped by himself, stretched his legs and shook himself so that I almost lost my seat. After which I set off at a gallop and, while still rushing home, I killed a large wild turkey which he galloped up to, as if trained for the hunt, and which I was able to pick up without dismounting.

"I had hardly returned to Dr. Rankin's, where I was staying, before I sent word to the horse's owner that I would be well pleased to see him. When he arrived, I asked his price. 'Not less than fifty dollars.'

I counted out the money, obtained a receipt and thus became the animal's master. The doctor, a most competent judge in these matters, told me smilingly, 'Mr Audubon, when you are tired of it I undertake to return your money, for—believe me—this is a first-class horse.' He had it shod himself; my wife used it for several weeks and found it perfectly good.

"When I had to go to Philadelphia to attend to some business, *Barro* (he had been named thus, after his first owner) was allowed to rest and suitably prepared ten days in advance. When the time for my departure came, I rode off at about four miles an hour. I will describe my itinerary so that, if you will, you may follow me on some map of the country, such as Tanner's, for example: from Henderson, via Russellville, Nashville, Knoxville, Abington (Virginia), the Natural Bridge, Harrisonburg, Winchester, Harper's Ferry, Frederick and Lancaster, to Philadelphia. After staying there for several days, I returned to Pittsburgh, Wheeling, Janesville, Chillicoth, Lexington, Louisville and thence to Henderson. But the nature of my business often compelled me to leave the highway, and I estimate that I may have done about two thousand miles in all. I never covered less than forty miles a day, and the doctor declared that my horse was in as good condition on arrival as it had been when it left. Such a trip, and on the same horse, may appear extraordinary to a European; but at that time every salesman had to make them more or less all the time, and some of them came from far-off regions to the West, and even St. Louis on the Missouri. In truth, they often sold their horses when they returned, either from Baltimore or Philadelphia, or else from Pittsburgh, where they took the boat. My wife, too, has ridden a single horse, at the same speed, from Henderson to Philadelphia. At the time, travel through these parts was relatively new; there were few carriages; and, indeed, the roads were scarcely passable for riding from Louisville to Philadelphia; whereas today, the distance can be covered in six or seven days, or even less, depending on the water level of the Ohio.

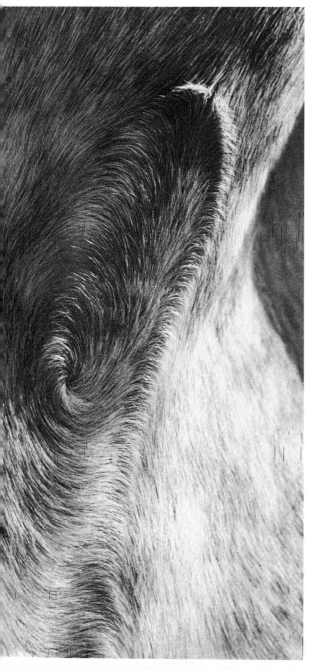

"Perhaps you would like to know how I treated my horse on the way: every morning I rose before dawn and began by grooming him, pressing his hindquarters with my hand to make sure he had not been chafed by the saddle; I then threw a folded blanket over him. The surcingle, below which were the pouches, held the blanket in place on the seat and a large and tightly rolled coat was attached in back. The bridle had a bit; a breast-strap with buckles on both sides kept the saddle in place; but my horse had no need of a crupper, as his shoulders were high and well-built. He set off at a trot, as I have said, at four miles an hour, and continued thus. I usually did fifteen to twenty miles before lunch; but after the first hour, I let him drink when thirsty. The halt for lunch usually lasted two hours. I made him suitably comfortable and gave him as much corn as he could eat. After that I set off again until an hour and a half after sunset. I then washed him, threw a bucket of cold water over his hindquarters, rubbed him down all over, inspected his hoofs and cleaned them. I filled his rack with wheat and his trough with grain; when I was able to get it, I added a good-sized gourd or some eggs; lastly, if the opportunity arose, I gave him half a bushel of oats, preferably with corn, which can sometimes produce constipation in horses. In the morning, his almost empty rack and trough were enough to show me the state of his health.

"I had only been riding him for a few days, but he was already so attached to me that when we reached a limpid stream in which I wanted to bathe, I was able to let him graze freely and he drank only at my command. He was extremely sure-footed and always so well-paced that, from time to time, when a turkey appeared before me from the place

where it had been taking a dust bath, I only had to bend forward for him to set off at a gallop which he kept up until the bird left the road and went back into the woods. He then resumed his usual trot.

"On the way back, when crossing the river Jamiata in Pennsylvania, I met a gentleman from New Orleans by the name of Vincent Nolte. He was taking his ease on a superb horse which had cost him three hundred dollars; and a servant, also on horseback, was leading a reserve horse by the rein. I did not know him at all at that time, but I nevertheless approached him, praising the beauty of his mount, a politeness to which he rather rudely replied that he would have wished me a like one. He told me that he was going to Bedford to spend the night there. I asked him when he expected to arrive: 'Early enough', he said, 'to prepare some trout for supper, on condition that you join me when you arrive.' I do believe that Barro understood our conversation, for he immediately pricked up his ears and lengthened his stride; Mr. Nolte, putting his horse through its paces, set off at a canter, but this was all wasted effort, for I reached the hotel a good quarter of an hour before him, ordered the trout, put my horse in the stable, and still had time to wait for him at the door, where I stood ready to welcome him. From that day on, Mr. Vincent Nolte became my friend; we traveled together as far as Shippingport, where another friend, Nicholas Berthoud, was staying; and on leaving he repeated something he had told me several times, that he had never seen so hardy an animal as Barro.

"If I remember rightly, I mentioned some of these details to my scholarly friend Skinner, of Baltimore, who must have put them into his *Sporting Magazine.* He and I were of the opinion that the introduction into our country of that variety of Western prairie-horse would generally serve to improve our breeds; and judging by the ones I have seen, I am inclined to believe that some of them could become suitable for racing. A few days after my return to Henderson, I parted company with Barro, not without regret, for the sum of one hundred and twenty dollars."

In Europe itself, horses are not always domestic animals in the usual sense of the term. In various places, they are left completely free for most of the year. This is the case in France, some English islands, Southern Russia, etc.

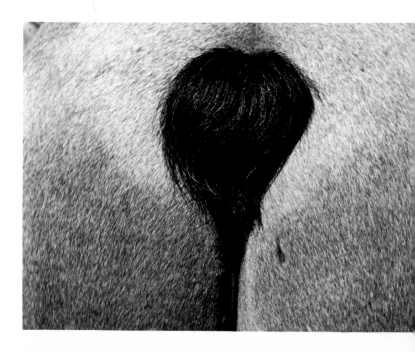

The horses of the Camargue (the delta of the Rhône), which are of Arabian origin, were left on the shore of the Mediterranean by the Moors and the Saracens when those people invaded the Gauls. They are of medium height. Their foreheads are square, their blazes straight and their heads rather bold; their legs are well-proportioned and have short pasterns. Their hair is very long in winter and affords sure protection against the cold.

Although *camargues,* as they are called, have greatly degenerated, especially since some owners introduced cross-bred stallions among them, some of their primitive qualities still make them valuable. They are both vigorous and docile; they are extremely sober and remarkably sure-footed. They live in almost complete freedom all the year round, in groups of thirty or forty, in vast swampy areas where they are left to roam free and where the only fodder they can find is rough goosefoot spurned by wool-bearing animals and grassy stubble which has dried up after ripening. In fact, springtime alleviates their miserable existence, for the marshes then provide ample pasture; but this excess of fodder occurs at a time when they are exhausted, and sometimes decimated, by the winter.

The camargue horse, therefore, is not the product of human efforts: it receives neither care nor rations from man at any time during its growth; it lives as it may and mates at random. But it does not spend its entire life in the wild state. Censuses are taken of all camargue horses; they all belong to owners whose signs they bear; and they all end up being caught, tamed and used for various purposes, although the memory of their earlier freedom often makes them dangerous.

Those which have been chosen for riding are cared for: they then become very vigorous, make fiery racers and obey their rider's will with remarkable intelligence. A camargue horse can cover 60 miles at a stretch at speed. This is one of the most nimble, agile and responsive breeds; it can be ridden over long distances without the rider feeling tired.

These animals may live for twenty-five years. The old ones are usually white, sometimes gray; but newborn foals are covered in a brownish down which falls off after seven or eight months: they only begin to look completely like their parents at the age of five or six. It is only then that they are first mounted.

As in the Camargue, herds of horses grazing in full freedom can be seen in several parts of southern Russia. It is only from time to time that their keepers gather them in, count them and pick out a few of them, returning the rest to their wandering life.

In Hungary and Poland, huge areas of grassland, mingled with vast forests, make it possible to raise horses almost in the wild state. Only the stallions are kept in stables: when the mares are in heat they know the road to the stables, which are far away for the rest of the year, very well: at this time they allow themselves to be approached and bridled without difficulty; when the mating season is over, they return to the pasturelands and the forests. The foals are born and reared without further ceremony; however, during the great winter frosts, hard pressed by hunger, they come with their mothers to the central stables for additional food, which is not refused them. In the Ukraine, the foals raised in this way become quite wild: they must be caught with ropes if they are to be tamed, and some can never be trained at all.

The same applies to the small horses living in the northern islands of Britain and known as *Shetland Ponies.*

"This is a small animal", says a specialist. "It is often surprisingly handsome, with a small head, a soft skin, a short neck tapering towards the larynx, low and thick shoulders (not a fault for so delightful a creature), a straight back, broad, strong haunches, fine legs and round hoofs."

These horses lead a more or less independent life in their own country, roaming through the forests and peat-bogs all the year round without being looked after by their owners, who only bother them when they want to catch and sell some of them or use them for some particular purpose.

For their size, these ponies have considerable strength. They fatten very easily and they are perfectly docile. One of these ponies, 9 hands high, carried a person weighing 167 pounds over a distance of 40 miles in a single day.

Norwegian, Lapp and Icelandic horses, like all the free-ranging breeds described above, roam in the mountains all summer long and find their own fodder all the year round. They are only brought to their owners' farms when their services are required.

Obviously, for these animals, there can be no question of improving the breed. The stallions mate with whatever mares they find, and their offspring are often of mixed blood.

So far as feed is concerned, these horses of northern Europe are not spoiled. It is surprising enough to see these little animals, which are so lively and gentle, happily eating lichen-stems hanging from trees; it is still more surprising to see them looking for wood on which fish have been dried. Like the other domestic animals of those areas, they are often given only cooked and crushed fish-heads in winter, and they grow so accustomed to this that, if allowed to, they will rob fishermen, taking fish laid out to dry and greedily devouring them.

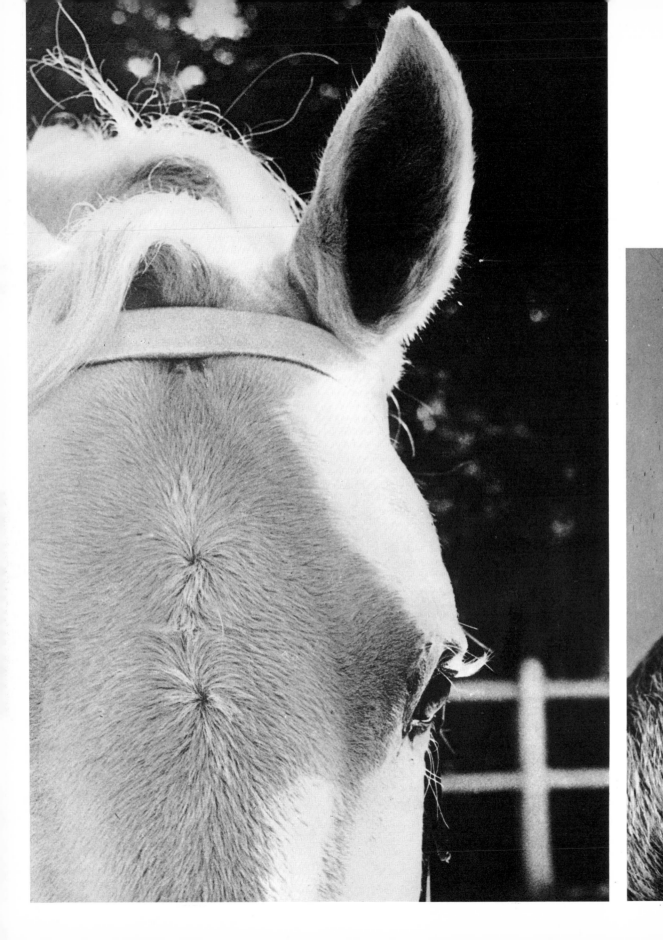

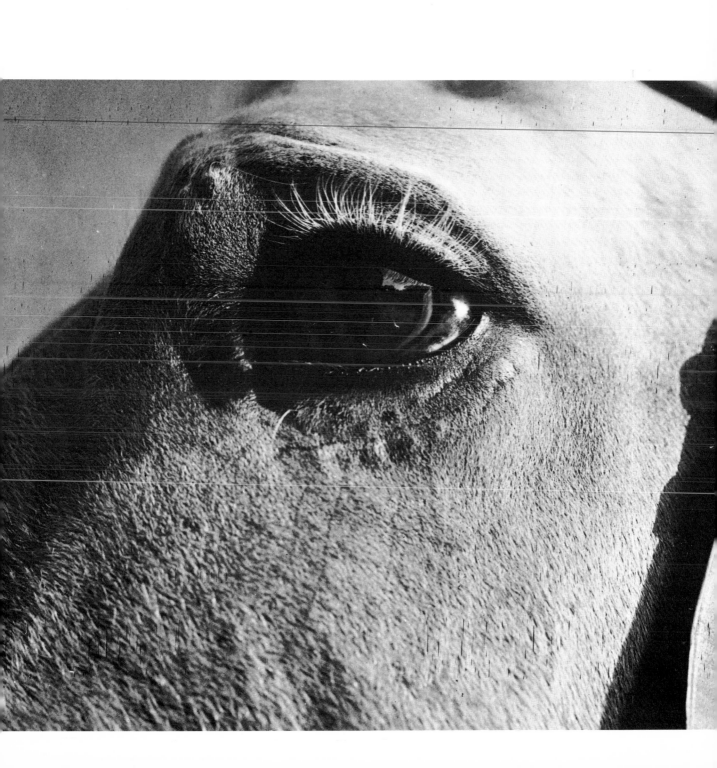

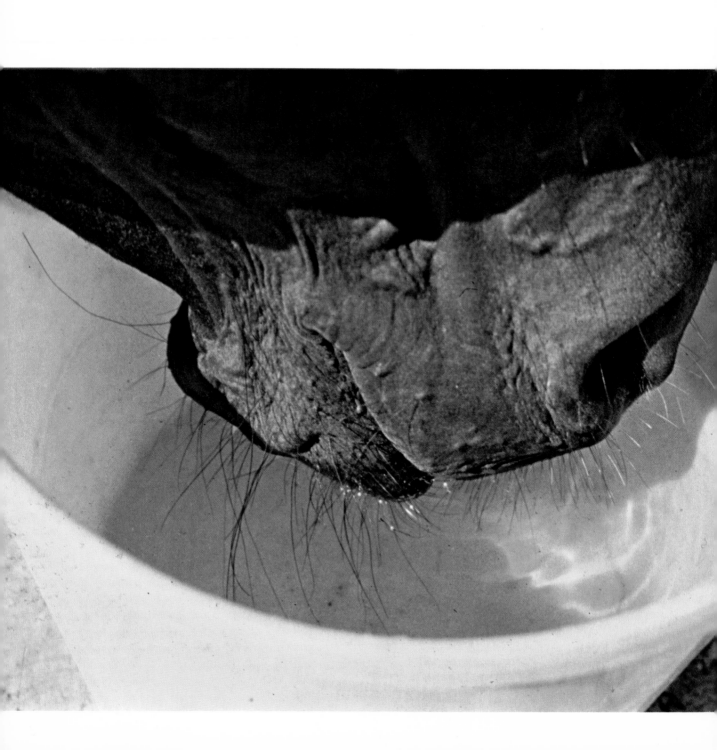

3. Domestic horses

The horses described above live in varying degrees of independence. Some die without ever having been subordinated by man, while others sometimes lose their freedom temporarily. The horses we still have to meet live in complete domestication and there are a great many varieties of them, as there are of all animals which are permanently handled by us, cared for by us and subject to our will.

Wild horses everywhere are similar in shape, size and coat: there is no difference between the *alzados* of America and the tarpans of the Ukraine or Mongolia. In both cases they are lively, small, high-spirited, bubbling with energy and sociable, forming herds of different sizes under a leader. The domestic horse, on the other hand, is a creation of man, a complex product of the earth and the needs of civilization.

The coats of domestic horses are of infinite variety. They may be uniform or mixed in color. The uniform coats, also called simple coats, are: (1) *white*, usually pale or silvery; (2) *black*, including jet black, light black and black proper, which is halfway between the other two; (3) *bay,* which is reddish with black mane, tail and extremities, and has seven distinct varieties: cherry, morello, golden, chestnut, tan, speckled brown and wine-colored; (4) *sorrel*, which is the same as bay except that the hair on the extremities is the same color as the rest of the coat, but which also has variations, such as a white mane, or scattered white speckles.

Multicolored, or mixed, coats are: (1) *gray*, including dark gray or dapple-gray, with black and white markings; speckled, black markings on a white background; spotted, with various amounts of black dotted around; trout-colored, with reddish markings; thrush-colored, with light markings on a gray background; mouse-gray; starling, dark gray; and pearl-gray, shot through with bluish-gray markings; (2) *roan*, a mixture of smokey white, light black and chestnut, which has five varieties: common, in which the three colors are mixed more or less equally; light, in which white hair predominates; dark, in which black hair predominates; wine-colored, in which the chestnut color is most prominent; and the black-pointed variety, in which the head and extremities are black; (3) *red-roan*, normally an equal mixture of white and chestnut, but with other variations: peach, in which the white predominates; light-bay, in which there is most chestnut hair; striped, a form of light-bay in which the extremities have black circles; milky, a mixture of light yellow and silver-gray; and black, sorrel or bay piebalds.

As well as their colors, horses' coats have what are called *markings*, which serve as distinctive "insignia". These include the *star* or *blaze*, a white mark on the forehead; if it runs from the forehead to the base of the head it is called a *white plume*, and if it extends to the edge of the lips the horse is said to be "drinking in its blaze". When this mark has black spots it is called "tufted". A *stocking* is a white marking on the coronet, and when it extends to the knee, the horse is said to be "high-booted". *Cowlicks* are areas in which the hair naturally grows against the nap. A *spear mark* is a natural hollow sometimes found in thoroughbred horses on the lower and side parts of the withers. *Bare patches,* pale pink markings covered with light down, are found especially around the eyes, the mouth and the anus.

Horses shed their coats, mainly in the spring. The long winter coat falls away and the shedding is completed a year later. Gradually, new hair grows and this becomes much longer in September and October.

In the domesticated state, this very thick and tufted hair is too hot; it is liable to become easily saturated with sweat and to remain wet for a long time; for this reason, it is the custom with thoroughbred horses to *shear off* this hair. The only hair to remain unaffected is that on the mane and the tail.

Feeding of domestic horses varies greatly from place to place, but its natural food always consists of various crops and grain.

The horse's temperament is basically sanguine and muscular. Thus, although it eats grass, it requires fodder with a high content of the main fibrinous and albuminous crops, such as grain, oats in Western countries and barley in hotter countries. Horses need more nutritious food than cattle because their stomachs are not as complex.

Although horses are less demanding than other animals over the quality of their food, they are happier grazing in dry prairieland than in marshy pastures.

In addition to the natural gaits common to all horses, whether wild or domestic, most domestic horses have gaits acquired through habit or training.

The natural gaits are walking, trotting, cantering and galloping.

A walking step is taken in four stages: A foreleg is lifted first, followed by the hindleg on the opposite side: when they are on the ground again the other two legs are lifted and put down in the same way.

The trotting step is carried out in two stages or beats: two legs—one foreleg, one hindleg, on opposite sides—are lifted and lowered together, then the other two, and the horse advances twice as fast as in walking.

The canter and the gallop are done to two or three beats. In a fast gallop, the horse leaps forward with its forelegs, followed so swiftly by the hindlegs that for a moment all four legs are in the air together.

Artificial or acquired gaits include: (1) *pacing,* a very extended step done in two stages. In the first stage, the foreleg and hindleg on the same side are lifted and set down together, the other two legs executing the same movement in the second stage; (2) *ambling,* also known as high-stepping, a kind of pacing in which the two legs on each side, instead of being lifted and lowered together as in pacing proper, are lifted and lowered one after the other, as in walking, so that three legs are almost always on the ground; (3) *racking,* a gait in which the horse gallops with its forelegs and trots with its hindlegs.

Here are some details, given by a specialist, of the way in which a limb is used for progressive movement in four stages. In the first, *lifting,* the foot leaves the ground; in the

Walking, trotting, ambling, galloping.

second, called *suspension,* it is in the air; in the third, *setting,* it returns to the ground; and lastly, in the *support* stage, it supports its share of body weight. When the four limbs have gone through these four stages, which may be reduced to two—support and lifting —a *full step* has been completed.

The two limbs of a biped, fore and hind, by acting together, each in a special way, are almost exactly like two pendulums: one, the raised limb, swings through its lower extremity, while the other, the support limb, swings through its upper extremity. Their oscillations, which start and finish together, therefore occur at the same time and at the same speed, but are not the same in their scope: the oscillation of the limb in the air is twice as broad as that of the one which remains on th ground. What the two legs of a biped do together in the same time, subdivided in varying degrees, each one does in two successive stages.

The support limb is the only one which can develop motive force. But it passes through three successive situations: in the first and third it is taut, while in the second it is flexed. Does it develop motive force in all three stages, or in two, or in only one ? This is a question which is too theoretical to go into here.

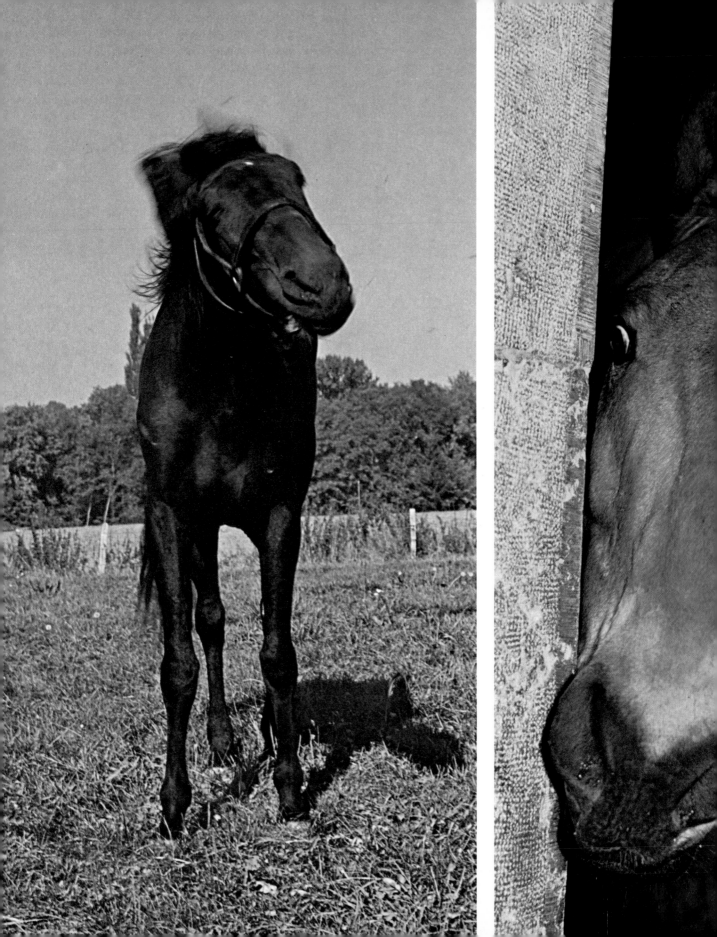

A horse's speed varies from 3 feet to 8 feet per second.

Horses have a concept of food, accommodation, time, space, light, colors, form, family, neighbors, friends, enemies, companions, man and things. They possess intelligence, understanding, memory, imagination, sensitivity; they are aware of their situation, and they are capable of feelings, love and hate. Their intelligence can become skill, because they are very amenable to training.

A horse's eyes are set in such a way that, even when grazing, it can see over a great distance in a horizontal direction; though not classed as nocturnal animals, horses can see in the dark better than men. In horses, as in cats, the interior membrane or *choroid,* which covers the back of the eye, is very bright.

Their hearing is delicate and they are able to receive sound waves through their large and mobile ears.

A horse's being and character, its present state and its impressions can be discerned from the movements of its ears: when walking, the tips should be pricked forward. A tired horse has drooping ears, while an active horse has strong and very mobile ears; irritable and stubborn horses have one ear forward and one back alternately. One ear moved frequently, especially if the horse looks to the right, to the left and to the rear, a wrinkled upper eyelid or a gaze that alternates between being fixed and uncertain all indicate a skittish, fearful horse. A horse which points its ears forward as if to "feel out" a person approaching it is gentle, confident and likes to be stroked. Horses with dry mouths are not as well-tempered as those with moist mouths which froth under the bridle.

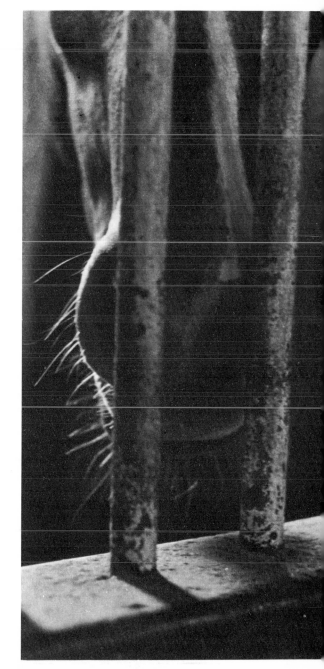

Horses have broad nasal canals and their nostrils can detect particular smells very far away.

Their sense of smell is extremely fine: they can smell a man approaching over a mile away, and can also sniff the existence of water from afar. In the heat of summer, Arabian, Tatar and Mongolian caravans and Spanish herdsmen take advantage of their horses' acute sense of smell to discover unsuspected watering-places. During the forty years they spent in the desert, the Hebrews often used their horses' instinct for the same purpose. American horses paw the ground with their hoofs to uncover wells which they instinctively know to be there.

"The horse is more fastidious over its food", writes a naturalist, "than other herbivorous species. Its taste is more developed, and its upper lip is capable of great mobility in feeling out and picking up food. Its skin is exquisitely sensitive, and it is able to wrinkle it in order to chase off harmful or irritating insects."

The noise produced by a horse's voice, called *whinnying* or *neighing,* consists of a succession of staccato sounds, at first very shrill, then gradually becoming deeper in tone, but still very pure and remarkably resonant. Whinnying varies with the horse's feelings, its wishes and its passions. There are five well-defined kinds of whinnying:

(1) denoting liveliness, in which the sounds become increasingly loud and shrill; the horse jumps and seems to be lashing out, but it has no intention of doing any harm;

(2) denoting a wish: long drawn-out and becoming lower;

(3) denoting anger: short, shrill, staccato; the animal tries to lash out, kicking forwards if it is lively, biting if it is vicious;

(4) denoting fear: low in tone and raucous, seeming to emanate only from the nostrils and, like the whinnying which denotes anger, short;

(5) denoting pain: a groaning, choking kind of coughing whose low, dull sounds follow breathing movements.

Horses have a highly developed memory for places and can recognize a route they have taken only once much better than their riders. They are sure of themselves and stubbornly resist their masters if they try to put them on the wrong road. The driver or rider can fall asleep with an easy mind, leaving the horse to find its way. Even after several years a horse can recognize a stable in which it has rested; sometimes, it emits a whinny of greeting and stops outside the door of its own accord. But if the journey is continued, it will calmly continue on its way.

Horses immediately know if they are mounted by someone who is not their usual rider and look round to make sure. They recognize their master's voice, understand his words and obey him. They leave the stable to go to the drinking trough and to be harnessed; they follow the groom like a dog, and return to the stable by themselves. They will look keenly at a new master or new companion in harness, and quite differently from the way in which a cow looks at a new door. They are interested in everything they see for the first time: a new car is an important thing to a horse. If a horse sees something which it finds striking because of its size, shape or color, it will run towards it, inspect it and sniff at it.

"In 1809", says Huzard, Professor at the Alfort School, "the Tyroleans, in one of their uprisings, captured fifteen Bavarian horses and mounted them; but later, in an

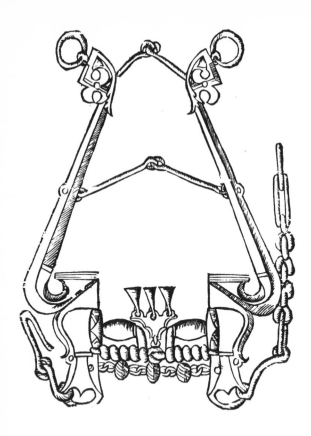

engagement with a squadron of the Bavarian regiment, the horses, seeing the uniforms of their former masters, galloped away with their new riders and, despite all their efforts, brought them to the Bavarian ranks, where they were taken prisoner."

The horse's intellectual qualities, its gentleness and even its kindness make it capable of learning anything a donkey or an elephant, for example, may know.

Elienus claims that the Sybarites taught their horses to dance to their flutes, and this was even the cause of their downfall. The Crotonites, knowing of this characteristic, played airs on a flute instead of sounding their trumpets during the battle: the Sybarites' horses immediately started to dance and to pass through the midst of their enemies.

Several early English authors mention a horse called *Marocco*, which belonged to a certain Bank. He was a horse of extraordinary skills and a prodigy at a time when little attention was paid to training animals. The poets, however, certainly exaggerated his capabilities. Delker claims that he climbed to the top of St. Paul's Cathedral. Peele assures us that he played the lute, a very fashionable instrument in Shakespeare's day. Some copies of a thirteen-page leaflet entitled *"Maroccus extaticus, or Bank's Bay Horse in Ecstasy. A Discourse in the form of a Joyous Conversation between Bank and his Animal, anathematizing some Abuses and Intrigues of Our Time, etc."* are still in existence. One copy of this satirical work was sold about a hundred years ago for the enormous sum of thirteen guineas. A wood-engraving on the first page depicts Marocco fencing with foils with his master. At his feet are two dice, indicating his skill at that game. Walter Raleigh wrote: "To be sure, if Bank had lived in the dark ages of ignorance, he would have put all the world's animal trainers to shame, for none of them would have succeeded in taming and instructing an animal as he was able to do to his horse." These words would seem to have contained a sad prophesy and warning. Some years later, Bank was incautious enough to seek his fortune in Portugal, where Catholicism was defending itself by the stake, and *Marocco* and his master were burnt as sorcerers there.

The various exercises which circus horses are trained to perform can give us an idea of the extent to which they can be trained.

A great many other indications of intelligence could be cited. "Horses", notes one author, "can guess the solution to a puzzle, answer questions by nodding or shaking their heads, tell the time by stamping their feet, etc. They notice hand or foot movements made by their master, and understand the meaning of a crack of the whip and of words; they have to know a whole vocabulary. When the

order is given, they can pretend to be sick, spread out their legs, hang their heads, fall to the ground, and play dead; you can sit on them, spread out their legs, pull their tails or put your fingers in their very sensitive ears without their moving, etc. Then on a further order, they get up and continue as before. And yet these exercises are certainly no fun for them; they prefer to run and jump. How long does it take to teach them to jump through a paper hoop which, to them, represents a wall? Who does not enjoy watching a circus? It is not the people but the horses in a circus that are amazing. It is not surprising that men should be able and willing to learn: what is surprising is that a horse can do so.

"To teach a horse to do something 'human', it must be treated like a human being; it must not be taught by force, blows or hunger, but by kindness, as one would teach a good and intelligent person. What works with people also works with horses. If, for example, a horse does not want to lift up its hoof, you coax it; caress its hoof, speak gently to it, reproaching it for its impatience and disobedience; you give it some oats, and try to lift its hoof while it is eating them; if it resists, the oats are taken away; if it seems to want them, you give them back and try to lift its hoof again, and so on. All horses which have not been badly treated in the past are trained in this way. As a rule, horses are just like children, with their good features and their bad ones.

"Horses have a sense of timing: they learn to walk, trot, gallop and dance. They are also aware of longer periods of time—morning, noon and evening. They have a feeling for sounds. Like soldiers, they like the sound of the trumpet, and when it calls them to the racecourse or battlefield they prance with joy.

An 18th-century horse ballet. In the center,
the Emperor of Austria.

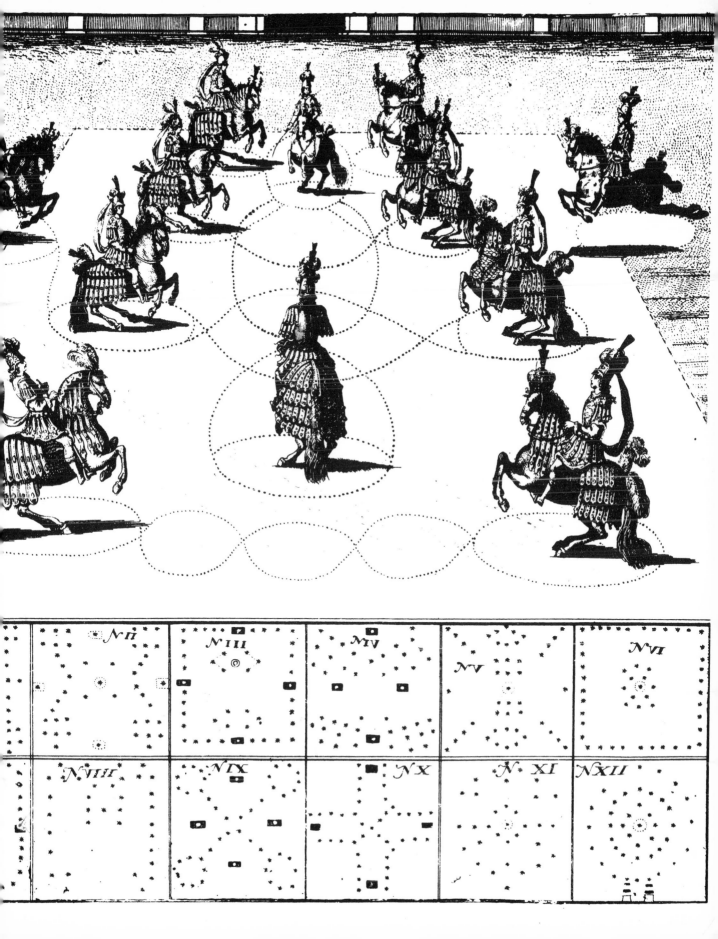

They know the sound of the drum—in fact, any sound which reflects their courage or fear. They know the noise of cannon but do not like it when they see their comrades hit in battle. Nor do they like thunder, and they tend to suffer in storms.

"Horses are prone to fear. An unaccustomed noise, an unknown object or a flapping flag will frighten them. They look carefully at stony ground and walk cautiously through water.

"A horse which had fallen into the foundations of a house under construction was brought out very frightened; yet another, which had fallen into a lime-pit, docilely allowed itself to be strapped and pulled out, even trying to help its rescuers. Horses tremble when moving through narrow mountain passes: they know that there is nowhere to hold on. They are afraid of lightning; and will sweat in the middle of a storm through fear of being struck by it. If one of two horses in harness falls, the other may save it, but usually fear also grips the second one and both horses, increasingly terrified, stumble and rush in all directions. What harm is then done by these animals, normally so peaceable, intelligent and obedient to their master, their coachman, women, girls and anyone who treats them gently!

"A horse can feel dumbfounded. It may be seized by a wholly fanciful fear, like a child, be frightened by something unknown or be deceived by appearances. Its intelligence may be affected by such things, which can even drive it mad. Bad handling, injuries and blows have spoilt many horses, making them foolish and vicious. Good treatment, on the other hand, raises their spirits, ennobles them and makes them half-human.

"The only pastime horses find pleasant is running. They are travelers by nature. In the steppes of Russia, horses gallop for pleasure for a whole day in the certainty that they will always find their way home. In Paraguay, they travel all manner of distances. In the grasslands, they move about excitedly, rear up on their forelegs, buck, race and bite each other. Some constantly excite the others. The young horses even provoke humans. A point to note is that animals who try to join human society in this way must feel that they are not very different from humans in nature, and must regard themselves almost as their equal.

"In a long and narrow Alpine valley, a young horse ran after a group of travelers, let them go ahead, galloped after them, went on a few steps past them, stopped, looked at them, ran back, pretended to start grazing, then followed them again, repeating the performance five or six times merely for fun, though it thoroughly frightened the travelers, who finally climbed over a wall that served as a barrier; the young horse came up to it, looking for a place to pass through and continue its teasing. But there was nowhere, so it returned happily to its grazing."

"What pride", the author continues, "an English racehorse develops! How proudly a general's horse bears itself! It feels its superiority; a king's horse knows its place of honor and demands to be honored.

"Horses are sensitive animals. They have enormous strength, their courage is beyond imagination and their eyes are ablaze with fire. Mares are quieter, gentler and more obedient and are therefore preferred to stallions. Rutting in horses is stronger than in other animals and accounts for their great strength. A gelding loses much by castration, but does not become completely impassive like the ox: it is more docile, more obedient, and is no longer prey to a consuming and sparkling fire.

"Horses are capable of feelings, of love and hate, jealousy, desire and vengeance; they can also be capricious. They live harmoniously with some horses and have bad relations with others; with others still, they will not mix at all."

The following story shows the sensitivity and devotion of which a horse is capable:

A farmer owned an aged horse whose teeth were so worn that it could no longer chew hay or oats: it was fed by two horses in the same stable. These two horses took hay from the rack, chewed it and then dropped it in front of the old horse; they did the same with oats, which they ground up into very small pieces and then gave to it. Several people witnessed this act of devotion, which may perhaps astound the reader, but is entirely true, according to an author whom we have every reason to believe is completely honest.

Wonders of devotion and affection are attributed to horses. They will bend sadly over the dead body of their master, look at him, sniff him and be unwilling to leave him, staying faithful even after death. In battle, they will bite the enemy's horses and participate in the fighting.

Examples often quoted of the devotion and

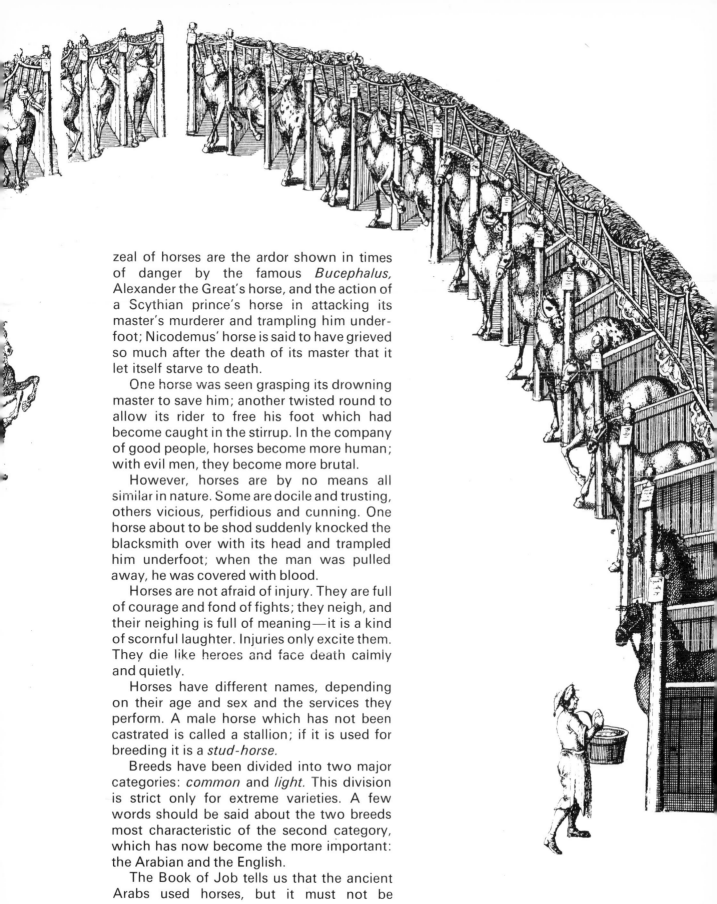

zeal of horses are the ardor shown in times of danger by the famous *Bucephalus,* Alexander the Great's horse, and the action of a Scythian prince's horse in attacking its master's murderer and trampling him underfoot; Nicodemus' horse is said to have grieved so much after the death of its master that it let itself starve to death.

One horse was seen grasping its drowning master to save him; another twisted round to allow its rider to free his foot which had become caught in the stirrup. In the company of good people, horses become more human; with evil men, they become more brutal.

However, horses are by no means all similar in nature. Some are docile and trusting, others vicious, perfidious and cunning. One horse about to be shod suddenly knocked the blacksmith over with its head and trampled him underfoot; when the man was pulled away, he was covered with blood.

Horses are not afraid of injury. They are full of courage and fond of fights; they neigh, and their neighing is full of meaning—it is a kind of scornful laughter. Injuries only excite them. They die like heroes and face death calmly and quietly.

Horses have different names, depending on their age and sex and the services they perform. A male horse which has not been castrated is called a stallion; if it is used for breeding it is a *stud-horse.*

Breeds have been divided into two major categories: *common* and *light.* This division is strict only for extreme varieties. A few words should be said about the two breeds most characteristic of the second category, which has now become the more important: the Arabian and the English.

The Book of Job tells us that the ancient Arabs used horses, but it must not be

thought that the whole of the broad Asiatic peninsula now called Arabia necessarily had this useful species. Strabo says that at his time there were none in Southern Arabia, including much of Arabia Felix, and although the excellent chargers with which their cavalry was gradually equipped made the Arabs' conquests easier, they had only very few horses at first. History records that the Prophet had only two horses in his army when he marched on Mecca to gain revenge on his enemies, and the list of booty which

Grooming.

he seized includes camels, sheep, silver and men, but no horses.

In Arab eyes, the most gifted animal is the horse: it is man's equal, if not to be prized even more highly. Love of horses is part of the Bedouin's nature, which he imbibes with his mother's milk.

Legend helps to raise the horse still higher in an Arab's eyes. He regards it as the most precious gift of the Creator. Arabs say that when the All-Powerful wanted to create the horse, He said to the south wind: "From thee will I draw a new creature which shall bear my honor. Condense thyself, set aside thy fluidity and take on visible form. This being shall be loved and esteemed by my slaves. It shall be feared by all those who follow my commandments." He was obeyed; He took some of the element which had become tangible, blew on it, and the horse was created. "Go and gallop in the plain", the Creator said, "thou shalt become a source of wealth and happiness for men; the glory of taming thee shall add to the lustre of the work which they have to do."

Mohammed made love of horses a religious precept: "Thou shalt obtain as many indulgences as thou givest grains of barley daily to thy horse."

An Arab proverb states: "Paradise on earth is a horse, the Books of Wisdom and the heart of a woman." The horse, it will be noted, comes first!

The famous ode of the Arab Omaya to his charger is further proof of the extent to which

horses are honored by Arabs.

"There you stand, noble charger, ready to gallop off, gleaming white like a ray of sunshine.

"The wisps that hang down over your forehead are like the silky hair of a young girl, swirling in the Eastern wind.

"Your mane is the wavy noonday cloud that floats in the air.

"Your back is a rock polished by a gently-flowing stream.

"Your tail is as beautiful as the flowing gown of the prince's fiancée.

"Your flanks gleam like those of a leopard about to seize its prey.

"Your neck is a high palm-tree under which the tired traveler rests.

"Your forehead is a shield polished and rounded by a skilled artist.

"Your nostrils are like the lairs of a hyena.

"Your eyes are like the stars of Gemini.

"Your gait is as fast as that of the roebuck that mocks the hunter's tricks.

"Your gallop is a cloud that carries the storm, passing over the hills with a long roll of thunder.

"Your bearing is like the grasshopper that leaps out of the fens.

"Come, dear charger, Omaya's delight! Drink the camel's milk and graze in the sweet-smelling grass.

"And if I should die, die with me! Your soul will not go down into the earth, it will also rise upwards, and then I shall ride across the heavens with you."

It would be impossible to include here all the minute details which Arabs take into consideration in judging a horse; we, men of the North, do not understand them at all, and our greatest connoisseurs are forced to admit, to their shame, that they do not know Arabian horses.

The Arabian horse is well-built; it is the best looking of all horses in form and elegance. It is medium in size, and even inclined to be on the small side; its lines are very wiry, though well-rounded and pleasant. Usually stocky, Arabian horses have a fine skin.

The most common coat is gray, which becomes white with age; trout-speckled gray is highly valued, and after gray, bay or

chestnut. Black and light bay Arabians are extremely rare. The hair is fine and silky, with wonderful golden, silvery and bronze-colored tints which are only found in horses of oriental origin and which have the brilliance of satin. In a few horses the skin is black, which enhances the beauty of these tints still further.

The joints are broad and strong, supporting

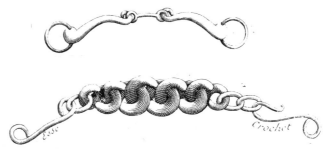

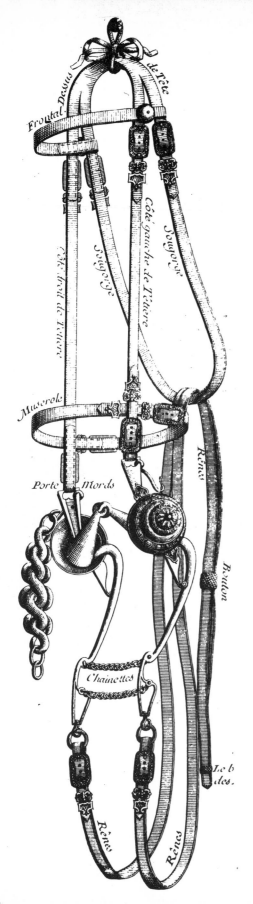

powerful muscles rippling below a smooth skin criss-crossed in all directions by jutting veins.

Seen as a whole, the head has a remarkable expression of gentleness and pride: it is, as it were, flattened, almost square and lean. The face is gaunt; the forehead is broad and sometimes bulging; the eyes, which are handsome and dark, jut out "with the expression of a lover's eyes". Black eyelids are a sign of beauty and the characteristic of a thoroughbred much prized by Arabs. The ears are sometimes small, sometimes rather long, but thin, well set, straight, slightly curved at the tips and at the same time very mobile.

A thoroughbred can also be recognized by other features. It only eats from its rack; it likes trees, green pasturelands, shade and running water, and will neigh on seeing them. It will only drink after stirring up the water with its hoofs or its mouth. Its lips are always closed; its eyes and ears are always alert; it tosses its neck from side to side as if to speak or ask a question. It is also believed that it mates only with other thoroughbreds.

According to the Arabs, these characteristics indicate a speedy, well-bred horse combining the qualities of the greyhound, the wood-pigeon and the camel. However, it is deceptive when at rest; its qualities are best displayed in action.

The Andalusian horse has remained closest to the Arabian type. It is courageous, agile and gracious. It has been highly prized since Roman times, and was long regarded as the premier horse of Europe; towards the end of the 16th century, Spanish horses were the best riding horses, combining agility and balance in the highest degree, as required in the *haute école* school of riding. This was

the horse most often depicted by painters. It is still excellent for riding and cavalry.

The peoples of northern and central Europe have managed to change the nature of horses profoundly. Should this be attributed to a more advanced state of civilization, improvements in agriculture, or other factors? Some have cited climate and food as contributing factors, and their influence cannot be denied. But the climate of England, for example, has remained more or less uniform, and yet the English have changed their horses so as to make them suitable for all types of service: after obtaining a large number of pure-bred horses, born in England, they crossed them with mares of less pure blood, and often even with carthorses. They obtained the "greyhound" of the species by breeding the racehorse; they also bred the enormous brewery-horse, and these two animals are as different as the best racing greyhound and the mastiff bred as a watchdog. The English made horses suitable for every kind of specialized duty—public service, fashion, sport, pleasure or whims. Almost all these horses have inherited some of their fathers' qualities of speed and their mothers' of coolness and good temperament.

A 12th-century English author writes of the races held in his time at Smithfield. Regular racing dates from the reign of Charles I and rules were first promulgated in the last year of James I's reign. Races have taken place ever since then.

The most important race of the year in England, the Derby, is run at Epsom. This major event was started (1780) by the Earl of Derby, one of the celebrities of the British turf. At the beginning of his career, the famous Lord maintained a magnificent stable with great ostentation and remained one of the

keenest fans of the sport throughout his life. He began his turf career in 1776 and was among the most influential patrons of the races at Manchester, Lancaster and elsewhere in the neighborhood.

After brilliant successes at meetings in York, Nottingham, Chester, Liverpool and Newmarket, he became a member of the Jockey Club.

Lord Derby won the race which he had founded in 1787 only once, with *Sir Peters,* the most highly esteemed stallion of his day, whose 284 descendants won a total of 4,084 races.

Right: A horse's neighing . . . set to music.

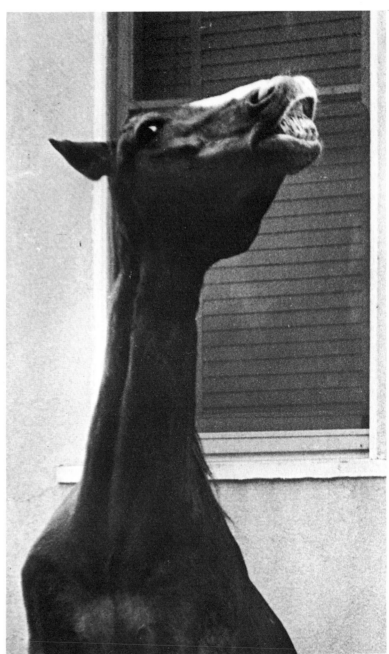

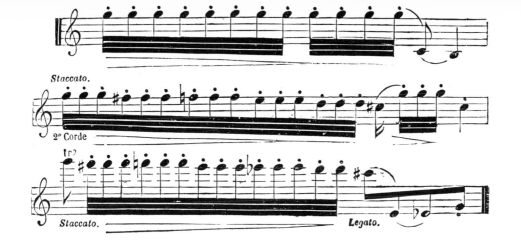

Dressage scene in the Hungarian puszta.

4. Training horses and some practical information

There are several stages in training a horse: it must first be tamed, and then, depending whether it is destined for the harness or for racing, it must be given special training: in both cases, the horse must be schooled or trained, and must, so to speak, serve its apprenticeship.

"Much attention has been devoted", says Jonathan Franklin, "in England, France and America to the art of taming vicious horses. The secret—if there is one—is very old. It is said that a bohemian called Con Sullivan rendered genuine service in this regard. Colonel Westenra had a splendid racehorse called *Rainbow;* but the animal was so wild that he had lost hope of training it. The horse would bite all those who came near it, both men and horses. The legs of any jockey who tried to mount it were bound to feel the frantic horse's teeth. Lord Doneraile told the colonel that he knew someone who would cure the vicious animal. The colonel did not believe it and a bet of one thousand pounds was thereupon struck. A messenger was despatched to Con Sullivan, known throughout the country as *The Whisperer,* because superstitious people believed that he whispered something in horses' ears. When he had been told of the animal's condition, he asked to go into the stables. 'You must wait', he was told, 'until the horse's head has been tied.' 'There is no need', replied Sullivan,

'it won't bite.' Then, he walked resolutely into the stable, after ordering everyone not to follow him until a certain signal was given. He closed the door behind him, so as to face the horse alone in what, I assure you, was a most unenviable situation. After a quarter of an hour had elapsed the signal was given. Those who had remained outside and were anxiously awaiting the outcome hurried into the stable; they found the horse lying on its back, playing with the tamer, who was calmly sitting next to it. Both man and horse appeared exhausted, but especially the man, who had to be given brandy and other stimulants. From that day on, the horse was perfectly docile and manageable.

"The following spring, another horse, *King Pippin*, was participating in the races at the Curragh, Co. Kildare, but its services had had to be dispensed with, since it would seize its rider's leg between its teeth and unseat him. In this state it was even impossible to put the bridle on. The Whisperer was sent for. He remained with the vicious animal throughout the night. The next day, King Pippin followed him like a dog; it obeyed the slightest command and allowed the first person to approach it to put his hand in its mouth, tolerating such liberties with the gentleness and docility of a lamb. It was taken to another meeting, where it won its race.

"The Whisperer's reputation spread throughout England. People vied with each other for his services. He is mentioned in several contemporary works. Crofton Croker, the author of a work entitled *Fairy Tales,* describes him as an ignorant peasant, but nevertheless pays tribute to his magical power. 'I once saw him', he says, 'trying his skill on a horse which, until then, it had never been possible to shoe without resorting to violence. The day after Sullivan gave it its lesson, I went to the shoesmith's workshop, not without some incredulity. Many others had gone there, too, drawn by curiosity like me. We all saw for ourselves the artist's complete success. The stubborn animal had formerly been a regimental horse and it may be assumed that when military discipline was removed no other influence could replace it. I noticed that the animal seemed terrified when Sullivan spoke to it or looked at it.'

"There are still many people in Southern Ireland today who remember Sullivan and his extraordinary power over horses thought to be untameable. The secret of that power has never been revealed. Science, while accepting facts supported by undeniable authorities, does not recognize any super-natural influence in man's relationship to animals.

"Cases have also been noted in which the wild force of some animals has grown milder and succumbed in the face of weakness. A farm in Kent had a horse which used to terrorize the stable-lads. One day, the farmer's son, a mischievous young boy aged six, slipped into the stable. On hearing this news, his mother rushed in, frightened to death; but to her amazement she saw the boy playing at the feet of the horse, which appeared to be submitting docilely and good-humoredly to the little rogue's teasing! The boy, who was already used to mounting horses, climbed up onto the fierce animal's back, using his hands and feet and hanging on to its long mane, while the horse submitted with majesty and kindliness. From that day on, horse and child remained the best of friends."

Schooling a horse, or *dressage,* consists of the methodical and continuous use of a variety of means, all of which are intended

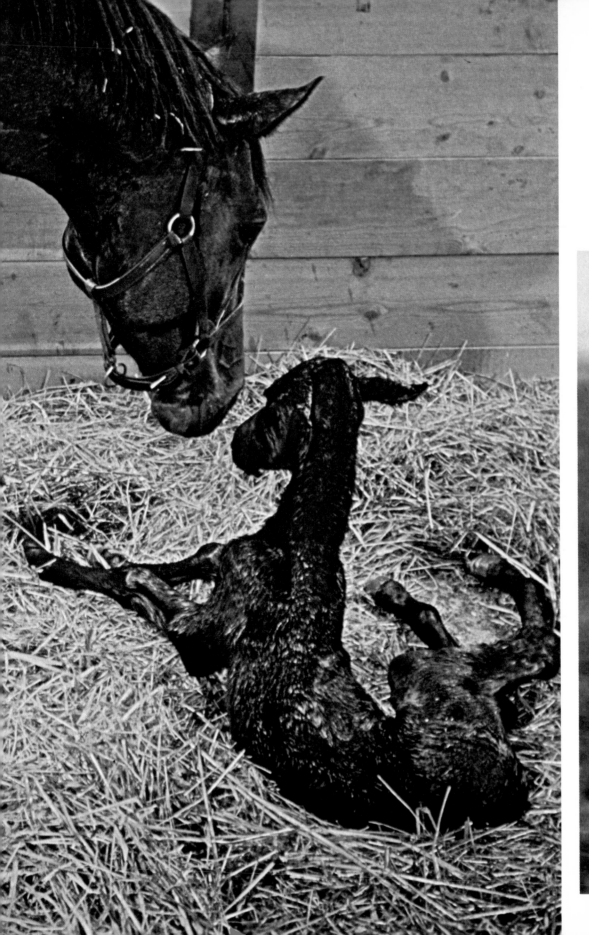

to bend the horse's will to human ends and to get its body used to patiently accepting the constraints and freely executing the movements which its future service will require.

Traction horses, like racehorses, require training. The most important piece of equipment for facilitating the trainer's task are the *cavesson* and the *dumb-jockey,* also called a *wooden man.* The former is a kind of leather bridle whose nose-band consists of a hinged iron brace (sometimes with jagged edges) with a halter tied on the front. The painful feeling which the horse experiences at the slightest tightening of the halter is a sure way of stopping wild movements of its head and forcing it to submit to wearing a hood.

When the trainer has accustomed the horse to obeying the pressure of the bit and to slowing down when the reins are pulled or speeding up under the whip, it still has to be taught to carry its head immobile and to be perfectly steady on its feet. It is now that the dumb jockey becomes the trainer's most effective assistant. This part of the training can be done alone, either in the stable or out-of-doors.

Horses which are to appear at racecourses are prepared by training aimed at making them able to run as fast as possible for a specific, but very short, length of time.

To do this, English grooms, who are great experts, use various methods; but they differ little from each other, and can be described as follows.

Only horses of English origin, born in France or the British Isles, are usually found in training stables. This is understandable; trainers accept foals aged eighteen months and two years, mares and fully-grown horses at any age. The time needed to train a horse varies: it may be two years, one year, ten months or six months, but never less. Rich owners employ their own trainers. Most amateurs send their horses to grooms who have made racehorse-training, a speculative activity that continues to be extremely lucrative, into a career. Throughout the entire training, horses cease to serve their owners, and it is expressly forbidden to allow mares to stand at stud. Everything else becomes secondary to the horse's nature, temperament and age.

Exercise and food are the bases of the English system. Horses in training are made to walk, trot and gallop; the trainer studies the strength of the horse in his care and acts accordingly: he nurses it, reduces or increases the amount of movement, stops all work when he considers rest necessary or else orders more frequent outings for the strongest horses.

Horses in training usually go out in the morning or the evening; the workout lasts for two, three or four hours. They do not work in rain, snow or high winds.

Greater and greater speed is required of horses as the day of the race approaches. Uniform, flat ground, without any uneven stretches, is always chosen for training racehorses.

Animals which are to be tried out as racehorses are always covered with one or more woollen blankets and wear leg-guards between the knee and the fetlock. They are attended by grooms who rarely leave them.

Once or twice a day they are rubbed down by hand, very thoroughly, for one or two hours. Stable-boys close the doors and windows and try to prevent the slightest draught. The horses are given thick bedding

during the day as well as at night.

Food consists of oats, mash, straw, hay and horse-beans. Average quantities are six pounds of hay, from fifteen to eighteen pounds of oats, very little straw and a few beans.

The ration of oats is given in six parts over twenty-four hours. Mash is made up of oats and linseeds, or oats and bran, mixed with a little boiling water: it is given to sick horses. A drink of water, by itself or mixed with a little flour, is given three times a day.

Trainers take great care to prevent horses' stomachs from growing too large: any hint of a paunch is harmful. It a horse becomes very thin, it is given frequent laxatives: the English use aloes, which they mix with castile soap. In brief, training a horse means making it trim, leaving it only the strict minimum necessary for fast, but momentary movement by wiry muscles.

If racehorses have engagements at racecourses which are far away from their place of training, they are transported in horseboxes.

Not all horses can stand training. Some become tired, unsound or crippled before the end; others become lame, and this affliction is then difficult if not impossible, to cure. Of every hundred horses sent for training, twenty-five, thirty or sometimes more fall ill with chest diseases. A distinguished veterinarian has seen horses limping badly or suffering from asthma immediately after a race.

In its broadest sense, farriery is the art of methodically applying an iron sole to horses' hoofs and ruminants' feet. In a narrower sense, the word means the *act* or *method* of shoeing, *all the shoes* actually worn by the horse or a *particular one* of these horse shoes.

As an art, farriery is divided into *hygienic* and *surgical* shoeing. The purpose of *hygienic farriery* is to cover the feet of animals used for their motive force with an iron plate, so that the points of their hoofs resist erosion by rubbing and movement. In *practical shoeing*, the form of the hoof and its freedom of movement, as well as the solidity of the leg's support, must be retained in their entirety. To do this, the farrier must: (1) model the shoe exactly after the contours of the horse's hoof; (2) adjust it in such a way that when it is in place the position of the leg on the ground is as close as possible to the natural position; (3) make the nail-holes as far forward as possible, to the extent that this is compatible with the shoe's being firmly attached, so that the nails hamper the springiness of the heels as little as possible; (4) leave the sole free in its movements and not subject to any pressure through the concave adjustment device; (5) retain the natural proportions of the nails by trimming them, so that the body weight is distributed evenly over the supporting bones and tendons; and (6) make the shoe of even thickness throughout so that all parts of the hoof on which it is placed remain at the same relative height.

A technician has developed a shoeing system to prevent horses from slipping, as well as to give them natural ground support, prevent crushing and constriction of the heels, navicular disease and several other conditions of the hoof which may be caused by shoes now in use.

Perioplic farriery, as the inventor of this new method calls it, has considerable advantages, resulting from the fact that the horses were made to walk *barefoot.*

Perioplic shoeing, which consists of the implantation of only a small iron bar, elastic

in form and more or less square, in the side of the hoof, is the method that is closest to the natural state, yet provides sufficient protection against the point becoming worn too rapidly.

We have said that it is not known when man first domesticated horses: but it may be assumed that efforts to raise and improve this wonderful living locomotive date from the time when it was first used in war. Horses were for a very long time one of the most powerful factors in the strength of States through their use in armies; they must also have contributed actively to the development of the civilization of peoples through the relations which they helped establish between them, at a time when our present means of communication between man and man, nation and nation, could not even be imagined, any more than the sciences which have given them to the modern age.

It is therefore quite natural to suppose that an animal which was able to contribute so much to the power of nations as well as the progress of their civilization and their prosperity must always have been of interest to State leaders. They realized that a people suddenly deprived of horses would immediately lose one of the major physical elements of its prosperity and strength; from time to time and in all countries, therefore, means of increasing the number of horses were sought and active attention was devoted to improving equine breeds.

This is proved by ancient as well as more modern history. In ancient times people spoke of the famous stud-farms of Solomon, from which the Arabs date the origin of their noble horses, just as today people speak of stud-farms in the various parts of the world where they exist.

In ancient times, Media (Persia) was considered to be the country where horses bred most freely; according to Strabo, it had royal stud-farms with up to 50,000 horses. Armenia was equally rich in horses, and sent 20,000 foals annually to the kings of Persia.

The term "stud-farm" is used to denote a place devoted to the breeding and feeding of horses; depending on the state in which the horses are kept, they are divided into *wild, semi-wild* or *paddock,* and *domestic* or *private* stud-farms.

In *wild* farms, the horses roam free throughout the year; foals born there are resistant to fatigue, strong and sober; but they are always stubborn and rather wild, and are never as handsome as horses born and bred under human supervision. They are watched over by men riding trained horses, whose job it is to bring them back to their owner's land if they stray. When some of the horses on such a farm are to be caught, they are all driven back to a given spot and the chosen horses are then lassoed and, when they fall asphyxiated by the tightening of the noose, they are fettered and a head-stall is put in place so that their training can begin.

This type of stud-farm can only exist where there are vast stretches of uncultivated land.

In *semi-wild stud-farms,* the horses live in the forests and pasturelands from spring to fall; in winter, they are housed in stables.

In *paddock farms,* which produce the best results, the horses roam in vast enclosures where they enjoy the benefits both of exercise to develop their strength and wisely distributed fodder. It is said that farms in hilly localities give their horses greater agility and that they are therefore essential for horses intended for riding.

In choosing a site for a stud-farm, farmers

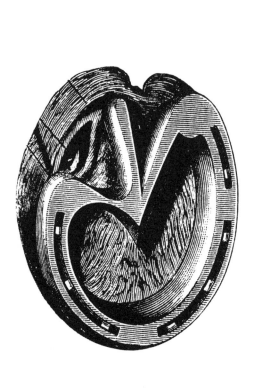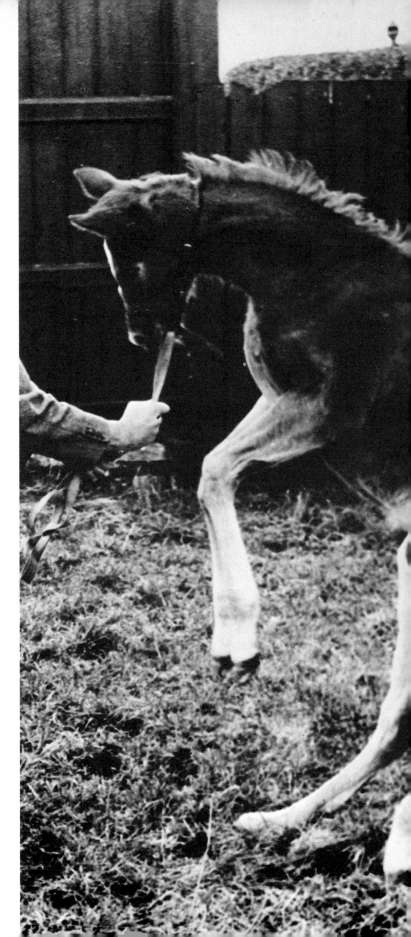

look for a place that has water and trees; the choice of site is important because it affects the nature of the animals raised there. Dry stud-farms produce sober, vigorous horses with hard horn on their hoofs; horses raised in damp ones, on the other hand, have large heads, thick bodies, poor-quality horn and flat hoofs.

Paddock farms are best because it is in these farms that horses develop to the full and can be best supervised. In large farmholdings, one part consists of grassland large enough to meet the needs of the summer months, while crops are grown on the other so as to provide grain and root crops for the winter. The grasslands are divided into large sectors, and the horses are moved from one sector to the next so as to prevent any loss of fodder. Horses, mares and foals are kept apart and cannot injure one another; all the animals can be trained more easily than in wild farms because they are used to human care and to seeing people.

Domestic stud-farms are farms in which

the horses are almost always kept indoors, only going out for workouts. However, a courtyard is always needed to raise young horses. These farms are inferior to paddock-farms and the horses they produce are much more susceptible to illness.

In *private stud-farms,* the horses are raised entirely in human custody.

Horses under human care live at the same levels of poverty and opulence as those who raise them, from those which sleep out in the open or under thatched barn-roofs to those which might be called the aristocracy of the equine world and which live in marble stables, eating from rosewood racks or mahogany troughs.

Horses in art: prehistoric caves at Lascaux, Greek art, Italian Renaissance, painting by Géricault (detail).

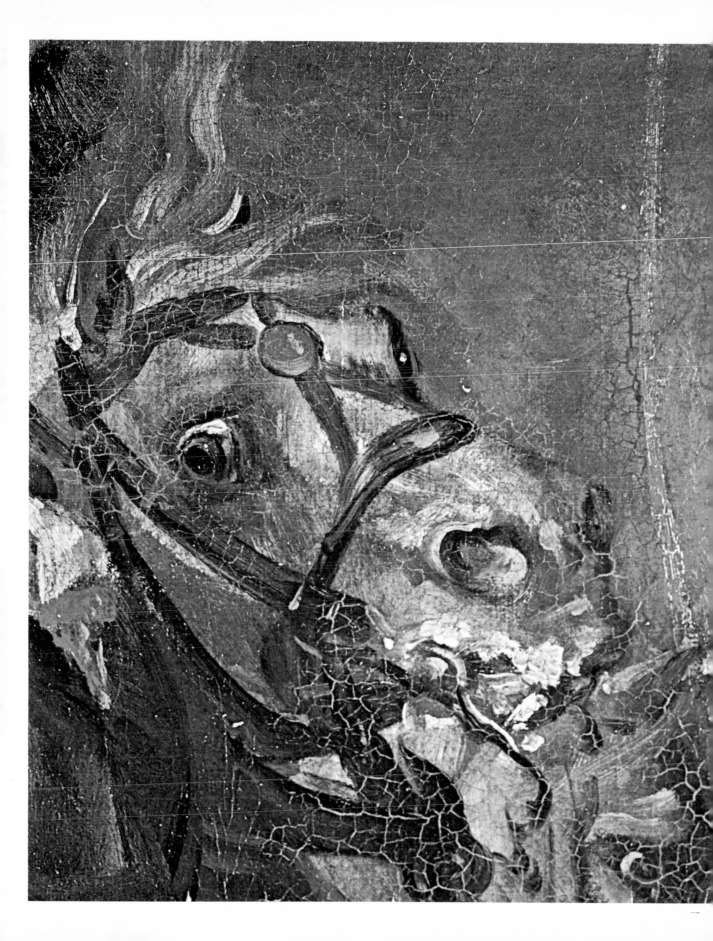

Drawings by Carpaccio, Leonardo da Vinci and Victor Hugo.

White horses play an important part in the theories of Sigmund Freud, who said that their appearance in dreams represents the positive forces of the unconscious.

Above: Drawing by Verrochio. Right: Illustration from a work on horses published in 1550. It lists the names of illnesses which can affect the various parts of a horse's body.

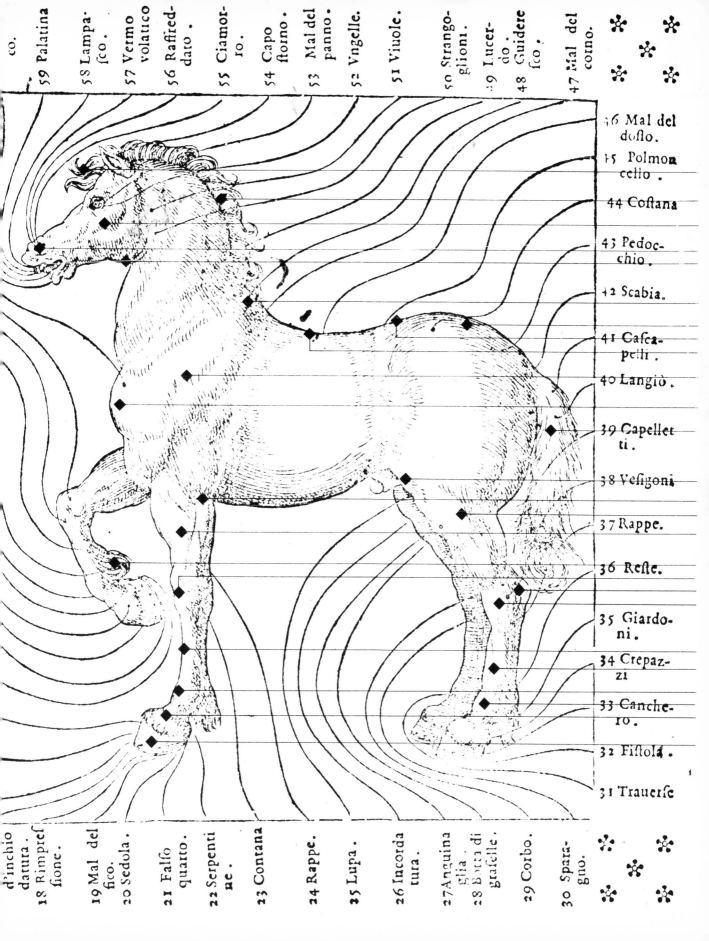

co.
59 Palatina.
58 Lampa- fco.
57 Vermo volatico.
56 Rafreddato.
55 Ciamor- ro.
54 Capo ftorno.
53 Mal del panno.
52 Vngelle.
51 Viuole.
50 Strango- glioni.
49 Lucer- dò.
48 Guidere fco.
47 Mal del corno.

46 Mal del doflo.
45 Polmon cello.
44 Coftana
43 Pedoc- chio.
42 Scabia.
41 Cafca- pelli.
40 Langiò.
39 Capellet ti.
38 Vefigoni
37 Rappe.
36 Refte.
35 Giardo- ni.
34 Crepaz- zi
33 Canche- ro.
32 Fiftola.
31 Trauerfe

d'inchio datura.
18 Rimpref fione.
19 Mal del fico.
20 Sedola.
21 Falfo quarto.
22 Serpenti ne.
23 Contana
24 Rappe.
25 Lupa.
26 Incorda tura.
27 Anguina glia.
28 Botta di grafelle.
29 Corbo.
30 Spara- gno.

5. The age and destiny of horses

In its first year, a horse is covered in woolly hair; its mane and tail are short, straight and fuzzy. In the second year, the hair becomes more glossy, while the mane and tail grow longer and smoother.

A horse's age can be told by its incisor teeth, which are situated in the following order, in the front of each side of the jaws: nippers or median incisors, corner teeth, central incisors, nippers. Together, these teeth form a semi-circle which deteriorates with age. Foals are normally born without teeth; the first to appear are two molars. The nippers come through from six to eight days, the central incisors from thirty to forty days and the corner teeth from six to eight months after birth. The maxillary incisors usually come first. The hollow mark has always been lost on the lower milk nippers at ten months, on the central incisors at twelve months and on the corner teeth at between fifteen and twenty-four months. At the end of two years, the mark on the upper pincers is almost completely obliterated, and the milk incisors, whose hollows have been worn away, begin to shrink in size; starting with the nippers, they become yellow, the gums shrink and the teeth loosen and fall out, making way for the permanent teeth. Permanent nippers come through at two and a half to three years of age, central incisors at three to four and a half and corner teeth at four and a half to five. A three-year-old foal should have four permanent incisors: a four-year-old should have eight. A five-year-old foal has lost all its milk incisors: its canines have come through, and the horse is then said to have cut all its teeth. All its teeth are hollow but, as with the milk teeth, the mark is successively lost: at the age of six, the mark of the lower nippers has become obliterated through wear at the edges; at seven, the central incisors have lost their mark; at eight, the mark on the corner teeth has been lost, and the horse is then said to have ground its teeth or to be "aged". But its age can still be told from its teeth. Thus, loss of the mark on the upper nippers indicates nine years of age, on the central incisors ten and on the corner teeth eleven to twelve. At the age of thirteen all the incisors have rounded edges and the sides of the nippers become elongated; at fourteen, the lower nippers are almost triangular and the central incisors become elongated at the sides; at fifteen, the central incisors begin to become triangular; at sixteen the process is complete and the corner teeth begin to assume this shape; at seventeen, all the maxillary incisors in the upper jaw are triangular; at eighteen, the lateral parts of the triangle grow longer, first incisors and corner teeth; the mandibular nippers are flat from side to side at nineteen, the central incisors at twenty and the corner teeth at twenty-one. After this, changes can no longer be observed.

At the age of six, the teeth are upright in the mouth, but this position is lost with age.

The average life-span of horses cannot be accurately established: it varies from country to country and depends on the habits of the nations using the horse. In general, horses may be said to live from fifteen to thirty years.

A horse may reach the age of forty, but it

113

is usually so badly treated that it is old at twenty.

Horses have been known to reach fifty (Buffon), sixty-five and even seventy (Pliny); *Old Billy,* whose head is in the Manchester Museum, was over seventy-two when he died.

Here is an example of longevity in a horse. The doyen of English warhorses, *Bob the Crimean,* died in November 1862. He had started serving in a regiment of hussars on October 2, 1833, had continued through long years of peace before serving in the Crimean campaign, had seen the memorable charge at Balaclava and taken part in the battles of Alma and Inkerman. On his return to England,

the commanding general forbade his dismissal and retired him honorably at the regiment's headquarters.

Most visitors to the estate of Tsarkoe Selo had no idea that one corner of that beautiful imperial property used to house an establishment that was unique in Europe and probably in the world: the Imperial Hostel for Invalid Horses which had had the honour to bear Their Tsarist Majesties. It is true that a similar home for the aged horses of ordinary grateful individuals exists in England, but it does not have a cemetery with graves and inscriptions, as in the case of the Russian establishment. The tombstones were kept strictly in line. Each one bore special particulars: the name of the horse concerned, the name of the ruler who had made it famous, and often the animal's dates of birth and death. Sometimes historical facts were added. Thus, on one tombstone, a Russian epitaph stated that there lay the horse, or rather *friend*, ridden by Alexander I during his entry into Paris at the head of the allied armies.

Horses are exposed to a great many illnesses. The main ones are *spavin*, a tumor with anchylosis of the tibiotarsal joint; *strangles,* or inflammation of the sub-maxillary glands; *mange,* a dry or running rash which makes the hair fall out; *glanders,* an inflammation of the nasal mucus which is highly contagious, even for humans; *staggers,* an inflammation of the brain; *gray cataract* and *black cataract,* both of which are incurable, and others. Larvae of the bot-fly lodge in the intestines and nostrils, entozoa are found in the kidneys and the eyes, and the skin harbors lice and mites.

The virus used for protection against smallpox originates with the horse, for cowpox derives from horsepox. Jenner asserted this, and facts proved him right. The virus is

communicated from the horse to the cow and thence to man; but as the intermediary is not essential for successful inoculation, horsepox was given directly to man and complete success was achieved.

Horses undergo operations intelligently, but methods of keeping them still often have to be resorted to. The *twitch,* in particular, is frequently used. This is a stick with a hole at one end through which is threaded a thick piece of string in such a way that it forms a loop on one side and has a knot at both ends on the other. The animal's nose or ear is placed in the loop and the string is twisted until it becomes painful.

Fetters are long pieces of wood with a

strap or band of flat leather at each end, which is buckled round the pastern and has an iron ring through which a rope is passed, thus making it easy to tie all four limbs, or only two, together.

"What a varied destiny horses have!" writes the naturalist Scheitlin, "Most of them, loved and fed oats when they were young, only get poor-quality hay and blows when they are old, and are harnessed to dust-carts. Yet tears have been shed over the death of more than one horse, and more than one has had a grave of marble."

In ancient and modern nations alike, horses have often been honored and have sometimes even become the object of an individual *cult:* the Hebrews sacrificed horses to God, as did the ancient Persians, and Herodotus relates that Cyrus uttered angry threats against a river in which a sacred horse had drowned. According to the same author, the Scythians also had sacred horses, and they sometimes burnt fifty at a time on the tombs of their kings, together with their riders; the Germani kept horses in order to read the omens.

Pallas states that horses were sometimes consecrated to the gods in various parts of Mongolia. In Siberia, such consecrations were ordered by the Khan so that the herds would prosper. The magician chose the horse to be so honored, and when it had become sacred it was washed every spring with milk and absinth, perfumed, decorated with ribbons of various colors which were entwined in its mane and tail, and then set free.

The emperor Lucius Verus had a horse called Volucris. Instead of barley, he gave it raisins and pistachio nuts, and he wore its picture in gold on his clothes. Once he led it into Tiberius' Palace, covered in a purple mantle.

Caligula's horse is even more famous than Volucris: it was called Incitatus. On the eve of circus games, the emperor used to send soldiers into the neighborhood to order silence so that his favorite horse would be able to sleep more peacefully. He had a marble stable built for it, with an ivory trough, a purple harness and pearl necklaces. It was served wine in a golden goblet. Caligula gave it an entire house, slaves and furniture; he wanted people to go and dine with it, and often invited it to eat with him. He swore by its life and its fortune. Everyone knows that he wanted to have it appointed consul and he would have carried out this extravagant plan if he had lived longer; but it is not as widely known that he raised the horse to the rank of a priest. Having appointed himself pontiff of his own divinity, he took Incitatus as his colleague in the priesthood.

"Horses", says Scheitlin, "have their youth in which to amuse themselves, their adolescence in which to be proud, and their maturity in which to work; in old age, they are lazier and are pestered more. They flourish, mature and then wither away."